Ken McNeil   Borders   Columbus, OH   111-5115

CYRIL RAY'S COMPLEAT IMBIBER
No. 14

By the same author

CYRIL RAY'S COMPLEAT IMBIBER
No. 14

Edited by Cyril Ray

An annual celebration of the
pleasures of the table

'Next to eating good dinners, a healthy man
with a benevolent turn of mind must like,
I think, to read about them . . .'
W. M. Thackeray

BEAUMONT BOOKS
1989

First published in 1989 by
Beaumont Books
an imprint of
Wine Buyers Guides Limited
278 Balham High Road,
London SW17 7AL

ISBN 1-871073-02-2

A CIP catalogue record for this book is available from the British Library

Designed by Roy Williams

Jacket Design by Bob Burroughs

Typeset, printed and bound in England by
Richard Clay Ltd, Bungay, Suffolk

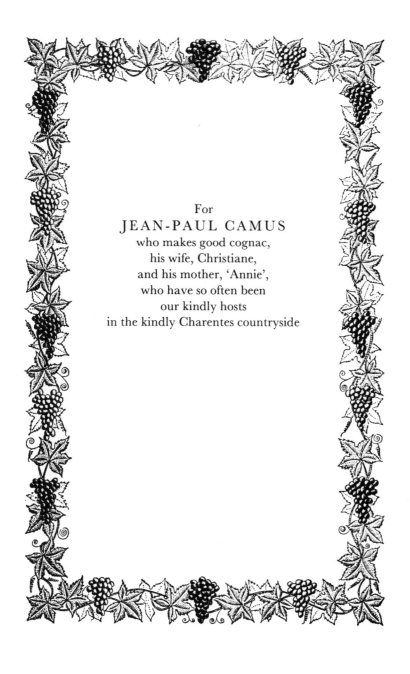

For
JEAN-PAUL CAMUS
who makes good cognac,
his wife, Christiane,
and his mother, 'Annie',
who have so often been
our kindly hosts
in the kindly Charentes countryside

CONTENTS

8

INTRODUCTION

KINGSLEY AMIS

'EVERYONE who takes an interest in drink,' I wrote some years ago, 'has reason to be grateful to Cyril Ray.' A gremlin, probably in the shape of a sub-editor not too well up in idiomatic English, or indeed any other sort, changed the second half to 'has *a* reason to be', etc., giving the impression that I knew the reason perfectly well, but was meanly hugging it to myself. So, since there may be some here and there still awaiting enlightenment, let me expound.

I suppose readers of writers on drink go to them in the first place for information (if not to admire the pictures). With wine columns now to be found in every newspaper; off-licence and other catalogues enormously expanded; television coverage and the rest, the inquirer is these days very well provided for, and British drinkers have become far and away more knowledgeable and discriminating than seemed possible even twenty years ago. More than that, a levelling-up process has seen to it that those educated in this department are no longer confined to an élite group.

There are obvious social reasons for all this, but it would not have happened in the way it has, perhaps not even quite to the same extent, without Cyril's influence and example. He won his commanding position by writing in such a way that those who may have gone to him for information stayed with him for pleasure. The wine encyclopaedia, the drinks handbook or manual, can be a valuable addition to the bookshelf, but it tends to be replaced there once the sought-after fact is found. To be read rather than just consulted a writer needs personal and stylistic attractions; it is Cyril's distinction to be able to exploit these without letting them run away with him as some earlier specialists have done. (George Saintsbury and Maurice Healy were admirable and valuable writers, but others besides me must have felt that there is a little too much of Saintsbury now and again in his 1920 *Notes on a Cellar-Book*, and of Healy in his *Stay Me With Flagons* of 1940.)

Another name for style is tact, the ability to make the reader feel at ease, not flattered or condescended to but, so to speak, fully included in the conversation. I am not at all sure how you do that. What I know is that all sorts of drinks pundits have not mastered it. Above the level of stark data, as soon as there are verbs in the sentences, the writer's self is there, all too often offering information in an over-erudite or patronizing or (worst of all)

9

chummy way. And some who should know better will tell you of the rare wines they have been treated to, the memorable meals they have been privileged to partake of, in a tone of voice that implies clearly enough that such grand occasions are not for riff-raff like *you*.

Cyril avoids all that because his attitude to his reader is comfortable and respectful. He also, what is no less hard, avoids the wild and whirling verbiage resorted to by writers grown impatient of ordinary language, who will invite their readers to taste paregoric, olive oil or asparagus in their claret, describe such-and-such a burgundy as philosophical, discursive, slap-dash, magnanimous. And not only writers: a man (a guest) at my club refused to speak to me after I had disallowed his description of a Muscadet as 'unforgiving'. Cyril has the imagination and the vocabulary to hit the spot without fuss. At a luncheon a long time ago, where he had chosen and was introducing the wines, he characterized an English wine (I had better forget which one) as pleasant enough but 'a little wispy'—and wispy was what it totally and incontrovertibly was.

If I had to choose my favourite among Cyril's books it would probably be *The Wines of France*, a well-worn subject revivified by anecdote, wit, and sunny geniality, an enormous subject fairly and perceptively covered in under 200 pages. But—to come nearer the point—nothing he has done, I think, has given more pleasure and entertainment than the series of *Compleat Imbibers* he edited in 1956–71. These annual miscellanies cultivated a territory Cyril made very much his own, that quite large region between drinks-writing or wine-writing and other kinds of writing, all manner of memoirs, sketches, gossip, poems, stories, bits of history, and general essays touching on the subject from the famous and the unknown. The *Imbibers* soon became a yearly publishing event, much looked forward to while they lasted and much missed when they ceased, and I very much hope we may consider them reinaugurated with the present issue.

As always in the past, Cyril has given us the benefit of his energetic curiosity and wide reading. The names of some contributors, rightly, are familiar in the context—Egon Ronay, Paul Levy, Derek Cooper, Cyril himself, Pamela Vandyke Price. Just as rightly you wonder at first sight what on earth others are doing here. What, for instance, could have induced George Orwell to depart so far from his radical convictions as to venture within a hundred miles of the realm of the gourmet. That small mystery is soon dissipated by finding that his subject is not *trockenbeerenauslese* but tea. And, after all, why not? Not for nothing is this the *Compleat* Imbiber. Next time round, look out for articles on koumis from Central Asia (fermented from mare's and camel's milk) and Ruou Tiet Dé from North Vietnam (a mixture of rice alcohol and goat's blood).

But I am not yet ready to leave the subject of tea. Orwell lays down no fewer than eleven rules for making a really good cuppa without mentioning the one I consider so essential that I always observe it when brewing up for myself: the vital test. It is to *make sure the inside of the pot is bone-dry before you drop the tea in.* (A paper towel is good for this.) If there is any water, be it cold or warm or tepid, hanging about at the bottom of the pot, the leaves will at once start to infuse in it, and tea made with cold, warm, tepid, anything but boiling water is very nasty and even a little of it will taint your brew.

You will see that Orwell also refers contemptuously in passing to 'army tea, made in a cauldron' as tasting of 'grease and whitewash'. Army tea of that era, and perhaps since, was made in what was called a dixie by throwing handfuls of tea into gallons of boiling water and stirring in a lot of sugar and evaporated milk fresh from the tin. I despair of persuading anybody who has not drunk it under the right conditions that the result of these gruesome-sounding procedures can be a dish fit for a king, or even a regimental sergeant-major.

Lord Carrington, looking back on an incident in his wartime career as an officer in the Guards Armoured Division, is also scornful on this subject. He remarks of what he admits was some not very good champagne, after it had been shaken up all day and half cooked by lying over the engine of a Sherman tank, that at any rate 'it was better than army tea'. I wonder. Or rather in his shoes I would very likely have plumped for the tea without any wonderment at all. But then even good champagne in faultless condition and suitably chilled fails to allure the likes of me. I sometimes think there are rather more of the likes of me than is usually admitted. By a process sadly familiar in human affairs, to be seen at work in such other matters as visiting the opera and getting a new stove for the kitchen, the thinking about it is much the best part, and the idea of a glass of champagne is much nicer than a glass of champagne, that sour, small, thin potation. Or so I would respectfully submit.

I was most interested to find both Sacheverell Sitwell and Evelyn Waugh showing enthusiasm for Mateus Rosé. I agree with Auberon Waugh that what his father drank throughout a whole summer might well not have been the wine some of us have known by that name for thirty years or so, but when he dismisses the latter as 'sugary pink fizz' I think he undervalues it as an introduction to wine-drinking. Plenty of youngsters and ex-youngsters, from among those unlucky enough not to have had a father prepared to start them on first-growth clarets in the holidays from prep school, have used Mateus as a staging-post on the way to more interesting destinations. And does anyone really want a seriously edifying vin rosé to wash down a summer lunch?

But to have touched on the subject gives me an excuse for a story, or rather a pair of stories. The great and good John Arlott used to give a splendid and highly circumstantial account of how Mateus came to be marketed in the UK. (The last line was, 'And he lived long enough to know he'd passed up eleven million quid.') I was retelling it once at a *Spectator* lunch to a company that included Quentin Crisp of *Naked Civil Servant* fame. (Beryl Bainbridge, being stretched out asleep on the dining-room floor at the time, presumably missed what followed.) I had reached the intermediate point at which young Luis, just back from a couple of years with a London wine-shipper, was summoned on that account to tell a group of Oporto entrepreneurs about the British taste in wine. 'To appeal to our oldest ally,' Luis explained, 'a wine must be pink, it must be sparkling, it must be sweet, and it must go with anything.' Without any pause Crisp said, 'He was obviously talking about me; I'm pink, I'm sparkling, I'm sweet, and I go with anything.' Take your hat off to that one, Oscar.

More recently, over coffee and brandy in the Gay Hussar, that haunt of the epicurean Left, I told John's story to the illustrious trade-unionist Clive Jenkins. Exactly as I reached the end of Luis's presentation Jenkins said smoothly, 'An excellent description of the SDP,' then newly formed. Now, our Clive will never be a political blood-brother of mine, but I wish I had said that.

Cyril will perhaps forgive me if I take the chance of making a point of my own before I sign off. Wine is undoubtedly a very large subject, more than ever now that it stretches from California to New Zealand. But surely it is no larger than all other alcoholic drinks combined, from spirits, beers and liqueurs to ciders and perries. And, here in the UK, those other drinks are drunk in much greater quantities than wine, even in these enlightened times. ·Yet when we see an article or newspaper section headed Drinks or Drinking, the drinks discussed, ninety-nine times out of a hundred, are wines and nothing but wines. It is true that, with new wines and new vintages constantly coming into the shops, there is always plenty to report from the wines sector, and that on the other hand a drinker of beer or spirits is probably not often on the look-out for new brews or brands. But there must be many like me who just occasionally would enjoy picking up a bit of information or comment about bourbon whiskey or Tasmanian lager without having to go to the specialist press for it.

Ah well, these wants of mine would be fully met if the *Compleat Imbiber* could somehow contrive to become a weekly rather than a yearly treat, and no doubt that is a main attraction in the reading-room of the great three-star hotel in the sky.

EDITORIAL NOTE

With this issue, No 14, of the Compleat Imbiber it is intended to resume, annually, the series of which Nos 1–12, (1956–71) have become a collectors' cult. In 1986, two sets were sold, one at Sotheby's, one by an antiquarian bookseller, for £400 each. Bought singly, each on publication, the twelve would have totted up to £20.55.

Nevertheless, an attempt in 1986 to revive the series with 'The New Compleat Imbiber', was an abject flop, in spite of its then publishers' studious avoidance of a 'No 13' in its title.

It was introduced by John Arlott; there were new, specially commissioned and written stories by Kingsley Amis (the year he won the Booker Prize); John Mortimer (a new 'Rumpole' story); Keith Waterhouse; Roy Hattersley and others, together with happy discoveries from writers in the past. Yet its publishers decided against advertising of any sort; the 2750 copies sold, out of a print run of 6000, were bought thanks to word of mouth recommendation or by chance discoveries in relatively few bookshops—some big booksellers never received copies. The rest were remaindered: any reader who enjoys this issue should look out for a copy of 'The New Compleat Imbiber' of 1986 —it should be a bargain . . .

C.R.

PS: Of the few reviewers who received copies, Lord Quinton damned it on television because, although entitled 'Compleat Imbiber', it was as much about eating as about drinking. One would have thought that the President of Trinity College, Oxford, might have taken it for granted that no imbiber is compleat without victuals to go with his vino . . .

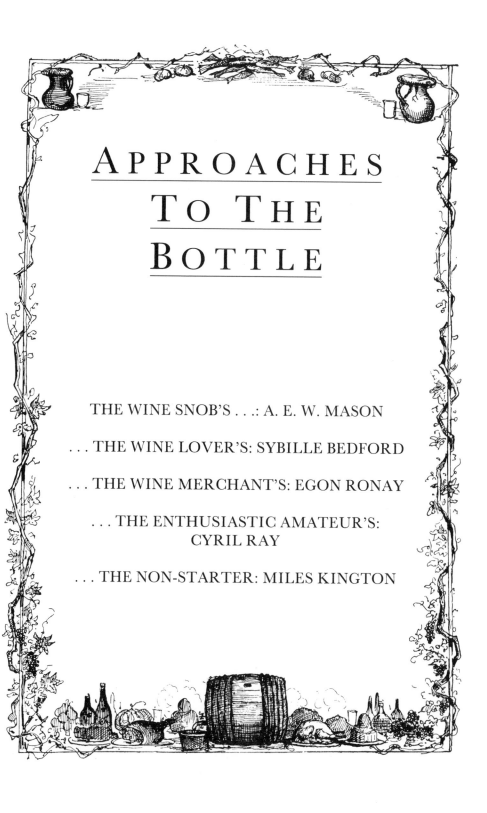

APPROACHES TO THE BOTTLE

THE WINE SNOB'S . . .: A. E. W. MASON

. . . THE WINE LOVER'S: SYBILLE BEDFORD

. . . THE WINE MERCHANT'S: EGON RONAY

. . . THE ENTHUSIASTIC AMATEUR'S:
CYRIL RAY

. . . THE NON-STARTER: MILES KINGTON

THE WINE SNOB'S ...

A. E. W. MASON

WHEN Mr Julius Ricardo spoke of a gentleman—and the word was perhaps a thought too frequent upon his tongue—he meant a man who added to other fastidious qualities a sound knowledge of red wine. He could not eliminate that item from his definition. No! A gentleman must have the great vintage years and the seven growths tabled in their order upon his mind as legibly as Calais was tabled on the heart of the Tudor Queen. He must be able to explain by a glance at the soil why a vineyard upon this side of the road produces a more desirable beverage than the vineyard fifty yards away upon the other. He must be able to distinguish at a first sip the virility of a Château Latour from the feminine fragrance of a Château Lafite. And even then he must reckon that he had only learnt a Child's First Steps. He could not consider himself properly equipped until he was competent to challenge upon any particular occasion the justice of the accepted classification. Even a tradesman might contend that a Mouton Rothschild was unfairly graded amongst the second growths.* But the being Mr Ricardo had in mind must be qualified to go much farther than that. It is probable indeed that if Mr Ricardo were suddenly called upon to define a gentleman briefly, he would answer: 'A gentleman is one who has a palate delicate enough and a social position sufficiently assured to justify him in declaring that a bottle of a good bourgeois growth may possibly transcend a bottle of the first *crû*.'

from The Prisoner in the Opal, 1929

---

* Mouton was reclassified by presidential decree as a first growth in June 1973. C.R.

... THE WINE-LOVER'S

SYBILLE BEDFORD

It is the early 1930s. Seventeen-year-old Flavia is living alone, with an allowance from her mother, in a small fishing village on the 'unsmart side of the coast: Provence, a fishing port'. She is working, with great dedication, for entrance to Oxford . . .

EVEN in the monastery, even in prison, there is a break of routine within the routine. Once a week Flavia gave herself a half-day off. On Thursday afternoons she took the bus into Toulon to do errands. She chose Thursday, the French schoolchildren's half holiday, because she liked the day and because it was one of deliverance for her, on Thursdays she sent off her weekly essay and work report to England.

*   *   *

At Toulon she collected a supply of money. Being under age, she was not able to have an account with a French bank. 'Can't she keep it under the mattress as you are all supposed to do?' Constanza had asked, but Michel got round the difficulty by arranging for the use of a safe deposit box which Constanza stuffed with cash. 'Take out what you need, darling, and don't forget to pay the rent.' But Flavia did not choose to run it in her mother's way. She insisted on a fixed sum for her keep . . . and on sticking to it. Learning to handle money, as she put it to herself, learning to do well on relatively little is part of the training for a life of independence. No weight of overheads, no clutter of possessions—no pot-boiling, no uncongenial work. So at the bank she counted her personal allowance off a wad of franc notes; this was the pocket and book money she had enjoyed, increased every few years, almost as long as she could remember. As naturally she was not expected to pay for her school-books the arrangement provided opportunities for nice decisions. 'Mummy, I've ordered the new François Mauriac and *Those Barren Leaves* and I'm putting them down to education. I hope that's not too unfair? I am paying for the *Guide Michelin*.' Into a second envelope went the living allowance which did for the cleaning woman's shopping bills and wages and her own dinners. She locked the box again, and after the bank there was the post office, a quick haircut, some soap to buy (good soap, one cake), and the day was hers.

18

Bookshops. A stroll on the port (When are we going to scrap all those battleships?). And presently it was time to give herself the treat of the week, dinner in a good restaurant, a classic French restaurant (once more, her term). She experimented now and then but her steady choice was *Le Sourd*, gilt, white and quiet. Elderly men dined there alone, unaccompanied young girls did not. As it had not occurred to Flavia that eyebrows might be raised, eyebrows, probably, were not raised. Even on her first appearance no one had tried to fob her off with Barsac and meringue. . . . At *Le Sourd* the waiters were old; they talked menu to her and gave advice which she took willingly if not every time. Her aim was to strike a balance between trying out new things and having what she already liked. If she ordered a sole with an elaborate sauce she might follow it with a cut of red meat, straw potatoes and watercress; if a grilled Mediterranean fish, by a fowl done in cream, going on to a piece of roquefort or brie and ending with wild strawberries. All of it was lovingly enjoyed but the big interest of the evening was wine. . . . That once a week Flavia drank half a bottle of good claret; nothing that she would have felt to be outrageous, nothing like Haut-Brion or Lafite, but something in the order of a third or fourth growth of the Médoc. She *had* tasted Lafite, pre-phylloxera what's more; Anna always insanely hospitable had fetched it up one day perhaps for love of Flavia's father. . . . She had heard much of her father's great fondness for wine from an early age, and of him she did think as she sniffed her '26 Chateau Beychevelle or Pontet-Canet. Flavia, too, had loved wine from childhood on. She loved the shapes of bottles and of course the romantic names and the pictures of the pretty manor houses on the labels, and she loved the link with rivers and hillsides and climates and hot years, and the range of learning and experiment afforded by wine's infinite variety; but what she loved more than these was the taste—of peach and earth and honeysuckle and raspberries and spice and cedarwood and pebbles and truffles and tobacco leaf; and the happiness, the quiet ecstasy that spreads through heart and limbs and mind.

from A Compass Error, 1968

> When the water of a place is bad, it is safest to drink none that has not been filtered through either the berry of a grape or else a tub of malt. These are the most reliable filters yet invented. Samuel Butler: *Note-books*

... THE WINE
MERCHANT'S

EGON RONAY

THE majority of wine merchants don't have good taste. They can recite exceptional vintages, they know all about colour, sugar content, or the previous year's price of a hogshead. But a good palate is a different matter.

At blind tastings they often excel. This overawes the observer, yet all it needs is constant practice and a good memory. It has nothing to do with good taste. An art historian is one thing; an aesthete quite another.

At the last Saintsbury Club dinner, the annual, formal gathering of the country's leading winemen at the Vintners' Hall, some truly spectacular wines accompanied food which, in a restaurant, would have given cause for complaint. At lunches for wine experts, the food can be bad or mediocre; and even when it's excellent, no one pays any attention to it. The deep sniffing is thorough, the swirling and lifting of glasses towards the light worthy of Marcel Marçeau and wines are discussed with the intensity of a post mortem.

Strange adjectives applied to wine echo around the table. But rarely have I seen any sign that winemen actually *enjoy* what they are drinking. There are no noises of delight or gestures of appreciation as in France or Italy. Only murmurs of clipped comment—one could be in a Pall Mall club. Conviviality would be in bad form.

The French adopt a more human attitude. Take the two septuagenarians with whom I was enthusing about a glorious bottle of Beaune, called Vigne de l'Enfant Jésus, we had just had with our dinner. Yet the two Frenchmen, universally respected connoisseurs in France, said not a word about whether the vineyard overlooked south or north, when the grape harvest had started in the year the wine was made, or who the château proprietor was. The moment belonged to delight, not data. In a post-prandial glow, one of my guests enthused: 'C'est l'Enfant Jésus en culotte de velours!' The other found this forgivable superlative: 'Cest le pipi de la Mère Vierge'.

By no means are all British wine experts single-minded. For example, The British Academy of Gastronomes makes sure that wine expert members are food enthusiasts, too. Hugh Johnson, its vice president, easily lives up to my two Frenchmen when it comes to untraditional wine critique. He, too, was in a post-prandial mood after an Academy dinner when, in his comments, he compared the texture of a rare Beerenauslese with that of 'intimate skin'.

Whether in food or wine, what is good taste? As in the visual arts, it's impossible to define, except negatively: consensus about bad taste is easier to reach.

Good taste comes both from birth and experience. Birth alone doesn't impart it, though sensitivity, intuition, intelligence and imagination—all inherited—greatly help to develop it. Dullards or thugs, for example, never possess it. Michel Guérard, one of France's very few original minds in the kitchen, is a highly intelligent man with an excellent education. Some great Chinese poets of the past were also legendary chefs. And food in Edinburgh, a city of culture, is traditionally better than in Glasgow.

More important than these gifts is experience. One eats with one's memories. Think what British school food has done to public taste—an impediment difficult to overcome in later life. Those fortunate to have grown up in a food-conscious household have indisputably much better taste.

On matters of food and wine (and in many other fields) I have always found women's taste more reliable than that of men. Women are more sensitive and have better intuition. The evidence shows in everyday shopping: most wine is bought by women (supermarkets sell 65 per cent of all wines) and look at the spectacular improvement in supermarket wines.

Sense of balance is an equally important ingredient of good taste. Amongst other things it differentiates a gourmet from a gourmand. A gourmet is a connoisseur who exercises restraint and self-discipline, properties that, together with balance, are tenets of the Greek Epicurean philosophy. A gourmand, on the other hand, is a hasty, impetuous eater, a glutton eager to stuff himself. But I suppose all of us who are passionate about food and wine have a touch of gourmandise in us.

Not as much, I hope, as Apicius in the first century A D. He was the quintessential gourmand: when he couldn't afford to live luxuriously any more, he committed suicide because he couldn't face a plain diet.

from The Sunday Times, 30.iii.86

L'EPICURIENNE

I was far from successful with Susie,
A highly imperious floosie,
Who said 'try me again,
But with *proper* champagne,
Because Susie's too choosy for Bouzy . . .'

from Lickerish Limericks

... THE
ENTHUSIASTIC
AMATEUR'S

CYRIL RAY

T HIS, I said to myself, is where I came in. In one hand I held a thick piece of coarse toasted bread, smeared with olive oil and garlic, in my other a glass of wine. That was only the other day: it was on a Tuscan terrace, the *bruschette* had been brought to us on silver dishes by white-jacketed servants of the Villa Ruffino at Passo del Pecorai, the wine was Ruffino's crisp white Galestro, cool and clean in the mouth. But I remembered how, forty years and a bit ago, and far to the south of this richly endowed Chianti country, as Eighth Army rumbled and grumbled its dusty, and sometimes disputed, way through poverty-stricken, war-ravaged Apulia, the peasants had given us coarse, oiled bread, onions sprinkled with coarse salt, and wine that was coarser still in grimy glasses—it was what they had, and we were glad of it.

That was the beginning of more than half a lifetime's love affair with Italy and her people, and with wine.

Oh, I had hero-worshipped Garibaldi as a schoolboy (and I do still) and as a journeyman-journalist I had drunk wine—though a good deal more beer. But these Italians, if not—or not all of them—in the Garibaldi mould, were men and women whose hands I had clasped and whose salt I had eaten, and this was wine that, I came to learn, was as serious and yet as simple a part of life as the bread and the salt—not the means by which a northern barbarian might boost his ego, boast his wealth or contrive to bed his girls.

There is a character in one of the venerable A. N. Wilson's novels who 'was never so undiscriminating as to suppose that after a bottle of Valpolicella and a glass of grappa all girls are alike', and I grasped easily enough that not all wines are alike, not even after a glass with the Italian girl in Algeria and a bottle with Amaryllis in the shade. That is the fun, though it is the fancier part of wine drinking. After our *bruschette* and wine on the Ruffino terrace, we drank with lunch an Orvieto, fruitier than the Galestro; a 1982 Chianti from one of the firm's estates; a fuller 1981 from another: and a deeper, richer Riserva Ducale 1980 that purists might have said could do with a year or so longer in bottle, followed by a lusciously sweet Solento 1971 into which

23

we dipped our hard Tuscan almond-cake, the name of which escapes me (no, it is not an *amaretto*), as is the custom of the country.

All of which was interesting to think about but not, thanks be to Bacchus, to talk about or not too damn much, for Italy is a wine-growing country and not, like Britain, a wine-talking country. The only wine-growing country that talks as much about the stuff as Britain does is California.

Back at home in England, with our much simpler dinner (a boiled fowl stuffed with prunes, onions and mushrooms, served cold—a dish called Hindle Wakes that Lancashire created and that Lancashire has forgotten) we drank claret, which I was glad of after so much Chianti, just as a couple of days before I had been glad of Chianti. The change was as good as a rest, and all the more so because there is no sniffing and sipping at the Ray family table, no rollings of wine around the mouth and of eyeballs in sockets. I think a couple of nods were exchanged: the 1967 London-bottled Ducru-Beaucaillou, if you want to know (opened only because I was back from foreign parts) was a drop of all right, which is all we wanted to know.

The only aphrodisiac, I am told is change. That is as may be, but I am readier to rejoice that there are more wines than one than that there are more women. I am glad that there is red wine to drink with meat, white with fish (not to drink red with it is inherited wisdom, not a wine-snob's shibboleth: fish gives red wine a metallic taste in the mouth; white wine will 'go' with anything, but rich meats overwhelm it into seeming mawkishness) and that there is sweet wine for puddings and bubbly for beanos.

I am interested to learn from an interview given to an American periodical by Hugh Johnson (whose books about wine have been bought by five million people who between them speak ten different languages, I should be so lucky—or so talented) that the 1981 and the 1982 clarets are widely different which I doubt that I could discern for myself, and that the 1980s are ready to drink, which I think I *had* realized. I should enjoy Hugh's telling me over a simple meal (nothing goes better with claret than cold beef, unless it is a cold saddle of lamb) exactly where the difference lies between the two later years, for Hugh Johnson is good company and an enjoyer. There are other, immensely distinguished, tasters who I think have never really enjoyed a glass of wine in their lives, just as I am sure that there are Shakespearean scholars, pontificating profoundly from this university chair or that who have never been moved to mirth by Malvolio or to tears by Lear. Their feelings about wine are expressed more in footnotes than in text.

They are making better wine now in the south of Italy than they were making that once-upon-a-time ago—in the co-operatives, at any rate, helped by government money and the outpouring of technical knowledge that sweeps around the world from the University of California at Davis. (What a *contadino* still makes in his own little patch is another matter, and I could down a glass of it with as much pleasure as his own.) They used to say in Lancashire, in the days when there was no need to hunt for 'real ale' because all ale was 'real', that there was no bad beer, but that some was better than others. I used to drink Boddingtons', because a young Boddington kept wicket for the county, until I grew up to Guinness.

What used to be good wine is better now, everywhere, on both sides of the Iron Curtain and in both halves of the globe: Australia vies with California to produce Chardonnays that can be compared with those of Burgundy, and the comparison can be interesting so long as it doesn't go on all night. A Cabernet Sauvignon from Bulgaria can be tasted alongside one from Bordeaux, and the differences are pleasing to puzzle over, so long as the puzzlement lasts no longer than that presented by a Times crossword, so that you can go on to talk about Tebbit say, safe in the knowledge that there is a sweet wine to come that will take the taste right out of your mouth.

It is nearly halfway now between those Eighth Army days of wine and onions and these of wine and occasional roses—getting on for twenty years—since Elie de Rothschild of Château Lafite told me, 'There's a lot of snobbish talk about the best way to treat and drink claret, but it's all great nonsense. The best way is to pull the cork out and lap it up. Claret's a pleasure, not a puzzling duty.'

*　　*　　*

> But hark! a sound is stealing on my ear—
> A soft and silvery sound—I know it well.
> Its tinkling tells me that a time is near
> Precious to me—it is the Dinner Bell . . .

By which I mean that a wifely voice is heard: dinner awaits and, this time, a litre bottle from a supermarket. Lap it up I shall, as if it were Lafite—lap it, and overlap.

from Punch Extra, 20.vi.1984

26

... THE NON-STARTER

MILES KINGTON

IF ALL had gone according to plan, I would by now be one of the foremost British experts on wine. Nowadays almost everyone is expected to be on talking terms with at least a dozen varieties of grape, and nobody is surprised when someone like Auberon Waugh suddenly turns into a wine consultant, but even in such company I think I would have stood out, because my training would have been vastly superior to theirs. The only drawback was that my training never took. I was brought up to be a top wine man and it was such an unsuccessful process that I have remained one of the most cheerfully ignorant wine-tasters of my generation.

It was my father's plan. He was a director of Border Breweries in Wrexham, north Wales, which had a flourishing wine and spirits division, and he saw me eventually moving into it and learning the trade. When I opted at about 14 to specialize in languages at school, he was absolutely delighted. It wasn't the fact that I would be able to taste Voltaire and Heine at first hand that delighted him, but the thought that I could sally forth from Wrexham and talk to wine-growers in their own language.

'If all goes well, you'll be an all-purpose European buyer and seller, Miles. Whenever I go to France or Germany to do business, I'm always aware of not being able to speak the language properly, but with French, German and some Spanish, you'll be ideal. Pity about not having Italian, but you can learn that later.'

The idea seemed preposterous to me. By that time I had discovered Voltaire and Heine and all I ever wanted to do was write like them, but my father was dead serious about it. For part of my summer holidays he used to send me abroad to keep learning the languages, and I almost always stayed with families connected with the drink trade. At the age of 17 I stayed in Koblenz with a nice German family and learnt about grapes before being sent on to a family in Wüppertal my father had visited before me; in 1945, as a matter of fact, as a member of the newly arrived Royal Welch Fusiliers who had, if my father's version of the war was at all correct, won it more or less single-handed with occasional help from Churchill.

'Those of us who had any specialist knowledge were kept behind to help get Germany on her feet again,' said Dad. 'Well, I was a brewer, and Wüppertal was a big brewing place, so I spent six months there working at the Wicküler Brauerei. I've written to the present head of the place, a Mr Bürgener, and he has agreed to let you stay for a while.'

Mr Bürgener was a large, gruff man, a bit like President Hindenburg, and he lived in a huge, gruff house all alone except for his wife and a grown-up son called Wilfried. All Mr Bürgener wanted to do was make beer and all Wilfried wanted to do was drive round Wüppertal in a fast sports car, meeting the other rich young kids of the town, while Frau Bürgener cooked meals for both of them. Wilfried must have sighed deeply at the thought of having to chaperon a shy, 17-year old English boy round the place, but he never let on—indeed, he was deeply impressed by the fact that I knew the German for gear lever, *Schalthebel*.

'*Dass Sie Schalthebel wissen sollten,*' he would mutter, '*das ist unerhört,*' and he would slam the *Schalthebel* into gear and we would whizz off to some other drinking club where he would have a good time with his mates and I would sit in a corner.

One day, though, Mr Bürgener took me off to the Wicküler Brauerei, which was an enormous place compared with Border Breweries in Wrexham. He was terribly proud of it, as he might well be since he had built it up in a dozen years since the war. The vats glittered and the cellars stretched gleaming for miles, not like the friendly but rather ramshackle Victorian building of Border Breweries, which might have benefited from being devastated by the German army and rebuilt.

'Is your father's brewery so big?' demanded Herr Bürgener.

'Not half so big,' I admitted.

'Does he have so many cellars?'

'Not so many.'

Mr Bürgener's satisfaction at having the bigger brewery soon started to turn to complacency, whereas I began to feel indignant on behalf of my father. Had my father not come over specially at the end of the war to get this brewery started? Was it right now for Mr Bürgener to have a bigger and better brewery? I did not think so. So when he started quoting production figures at me, I started doubling them and passing them off as Border's. Did Wicküler produce 10,000 barrels a week? Then Border did 20,000, and so on. Mr Bürgener's brow grew quite furrowed with the attempt to understand how a Welsh brewery half the size of his could effortlessly produce twice as much beer.

About this time my father began to transfer his ambitions to my younger brother, Stewart, who seemed to show more willingness to learn. He packed both of us off on a holiday, in 1961, to learn something about wine by going grape-picking. Dad had got to know the Sichel family a bit, and secured two jobs for us at Château Palmer in the Bordeaux area, so Stewart and I set off on his 250cc Vespa across France, to arrive there in time for the vendange.

We stayed at small fishing ports in Brittany, drifted through trendy La Baule and overnighted at the YMCA at Saintes, where I played table tennis with a bearded and sandalled young Parisian whom Stewart and I nicknamed Jesus. He turned out to be a carpenter, which seemed apt, and as we played kept crying: '*Mouvement! Mouvement!*' I obliged by playing harder and harder, but each time he cried out the same appeal again, until Stewart pointed out that what he was actually saying was: '*Doucement! Doucement!*'

About Château Palmer itself I remember very little. A cute little château with two peacocks in the gravelly garden and an enormous kitchen where we got bread and coffee in the morning. Myself picking grapes, hopelessly lagging behind the 16-year-old girls who'd been doing it for years, and Stewart with a big wooden basket on his back taking the grapes away. Eating outdoors in the evening with the sixteen-year-old girls and their families, and trying to flirt with them, except they were better at that too, having done it for years. But the fact that we were working in one of the great, great vineyards of the world, and that Château Palmer 1961 is something you would now pay a fortune for—of all that I had not the faintest idea. What I remember about Château Palmer 1961 is getting there and coming back.

Now, how is it that I could have had such a perfect background and grooming for a career as a man-about-drinks and made such a mess of it? How did my brother, who even went on to study brewing for a year at Heriot-Watt in Edinburgh, leave the trade to become a cameraman and a farmer, and to spend most of the 1980s not touching alcohol at all?

I really don't know the answer, nor do I feel at all upset by my ignorance.

I have a sneaking sympathy with the character in Iris Murdoch's *The Sea, The Sea* who, somewhere in the first 20 pages (I couldn't get any further) says that he refuses to become educated in wine appreciation—the only result is that your standards grow higher and you pay more money to get the same pleasure. I have no envy of my friend Barlow, who is the nearest thing I know to a wine buff, the kind of man who likes to have an anonymous glass thrust in his hand and to be challenged to name it, which he normally does after those facial contortions seen otherwise only on rabbits of a nervous disposition. Recently I bought a bottle of wine for the sole purpose of challenging Barlow to name the country of origin. (Difficult: it was Wales.)

'Well,' he said, pursing his lips, pushing the wine through strange internal tubes and trying to see the label, behind my back, 'it's a wine from a cold country. You can tell that, because it doesn't have enough natural sweetness, so they've added up to the maximum permitted amount of *Süssreserv*. That's the additive approved of by the EEC,' he kindly explained.

'How can you tell they've added it?'

'You can taste it. So it's an EEC country, coldish, northernish, probably hilly. The grape is probably Müller-Thurgau.'

I looked at the label. It was Müller-Thurgau.

'But I don't think it's a Germanic country. I think it's England.'

How near can you get? It broke my heart to shake my head firmly, deep inside knowing he had scored a moral victory. Naming the country of origin is child's play to someone like my friend Barlow, who would much rather be asked to name the grape variety—indeed, he is now beyond that into naming the kind of container in which the wine has been matured. I have had all these things explained to me so often that I should by now be able to out-Barlow anyone, but I can't.

Is it possible to be wine-deaf, as other people are tone-deaf? I may be. I once drank a glass of Château Palmer from some wonderful mid-1960s vintage, and have to say I found it muddy and inky.

I can, though, tell a glass of good beer from a glass of bad beer. I tried a pint of something made by Whitbread called Welsh Bitter the other day, when I was feeling very thirsty in Chepstow, and it was so sublimely tasteless and boring that my thirst magically vanished after the first gulp. On the other hand, when I first went to Southwold 20 years ago and had Adnams I knew without being told that I had just encountered one of the great beers. I was drinking a pint of lemonade shandy at the Crown Hotel, I remember, and there was a peculiar taste in it. Not unpleasant, but peculiar. Eventually I identified it: hops. I had never met a beer with enough character to get its hoppy taste through a pint of shandy before, and I hardly have since, which is one of the many reasons why I have been back to Southwold on holiday every year for the past twenty.

30

The Crown had changed dramatically last year; from a drowsy, elderly hotel into a wine bar and restaurant that London would be proud of, and I was lucky enough to gain an audience with Simon Loftus, the man who has done so much to make Adnams as famous for wine as it is for beer. He has a small room overlooking Southwold's rooftops, converted into a wine-tasting den, not unlike a cheerful laboratory, where he invited us for a canter through some of the wines he is fondest of.

It took me straight back to Border Breweries, where my father would vanish to the sample cellar at the slightest hint that lunchtime was approaching, except that the sample cellar was deep in the earth, a simple, white-painted, vaulted room where the latest barrels were racked and waiting for the bosses to draw off a sample pint. My father's colleagues wouldn't even have recognized Simon Loftus as being a member of the same trade.

Loftus apologized for his lack of a way with words. He needn't have done. Just as a red wine gradually becomes more friendly and expansive after being uncorked, he started to be carried away by the romance of wine-making and by the stories that lay behind each bottle, until after about 20 minutes he was telling tales like an old wizard.

But I made enough notes to remind myself that each wine contained a human, personal story. The Colombard, Vin de Pays, Côtes de Gascogne, for instance—this was made by a co-operative in Gascony who were lumbered with enormous quantities of wine from the Colombard grape, and instead of sitting down and crying, travelled the globe looking for a technical solution until they found it in, of all places, California. Simon Loftus had introduced their wine into England and designed a new label for it which had been so successful that the co-operative were now using his label in France . . .

Or something like that. What was patently obvious to me was that along with all the characters he mentioned—the Professor of Viticulture at Bordeaux and his pink wine; the peasant bloke; the men from the Côtes du Rhone who came to Southwold in February and did a combined wine and apricot deal; the Burgundy grower and his American wife, Pamela—Loftus himself was as much of a character. The extraordinary thing was that he could date precisely the start of his interest in wine.

'My father, who also was involved in Adnams Brewery, had a good wine cellar which was unfortunately flooded during the great east-coast floods of 1953. The wine wasn't affected, but all the labels were washed off, which meant that you couldn't identify any of them. So he decided to drink his way through them over the next year, putting a name to them as he went. I remember being given a Mouton-Rothschild of some great year and being told what a great wine it was, and I can remember distinctly, although only a small boy, knowing instinctively that it was a great wine and yet at the same time that there was something badly wrong with it. It was only much later that I realized what it was—we were drinking it long before it had matured—but I am sure of this feeling that I knew, at the time, something was wrong.'

I also learnt from Simon Loftus on that sunny day up in his little wine eyrie what it is that wine merchants chiefly fear and resent: the arrival of friends bearing bottles of wine they have picked up on holiday, insisting that this great discovery should be tasted. They are, said Loftus firmly, almost without exception dreadful. It was at this embarrassing point that I produced a bottle of red wine I had picked up on holiday, a Comte de Toulonnais, from the south-west, on sale at a wayside wine shrine near La Roche-Bernard in Brittany, and it says a lot for Loftus's tolerance that he agreed to taste it. He sipped and gesticulated, spat and reflected. After a tense silence, he came out with the nearest thing to a compliment I could have hoped for: 'Hmm, it has none of the expected defects.' He even sent for Hugh Johnson's *Wine Atlas of the World* to look up this unknown Comte de Toulonnais* and found it listed in a footnote so terse that he commented: 'It's pretty clear to

---

* Comté Tolosan? C.R.

me that even Hugh Johnson himself hasn't tasted this one, though he doesn't admit it.'

I don't suppose it ever occurred to Simon Loftus that day last July that he was helping me to exorcise a small shadow of guilt. Here, at last, was the son of a brewer who had done just what I was supposed to have done. He had become drawn into the wine world and made his small brewery famous for its wines but far from making me feel that I should have done the same, he gives me the comforting illusion that he has done it *instead* of me. I can now go on being wine-deaf without a pang of conscience.

And if I *had* decided to go into the brewery after my father, I would now be without a job. Two years ago Border Breweries were taken over by Marston's, and the old friendly brewery, with the railway line running on a bridge across it and the red Ruabon brick chimney towering above it, was closed down. This Christmas it was set on fire, probably by homeless squatters, and is now a gutted derelict site, no longer steaming, smelling of yeast day and night, and resounding to the crash of rolling barrels. It looks just as the Wicküler Brauerei in Wüppertal must have looked in 1945, in fact, but this time I'm glad my father wasn't around to see it.

from The Times, 28.ii.87

THE GOURMET'S LOVE-SONG

P. G. WODEHOUSE

How strange is Love; I am not one
  Who Cupid's power belittles,
For Cupid 'tis who makes me shun
  My customary victuals.
Oh, EFFIE, since that painful scene
  That left me broken-hearted,
My appetite, erstwhile so keen,
  Has utterly departed.

My form, my friends observe with pain,
  Is growing daily thinner.
Love only occupies the brain
  That once could think of dinner.
Around me myriad waiters flit,
  With meat and drink to ply men;
Alone, disconsolate, I sit,
  And feed on thoughts of Hymen.

The kindly waiters hear my groan,
  They strive to charm with curry;
They tempt me with a devilled bone—
  I beg them not to worry.
Soup, whitebait, entrées, fricassees,
  They bring me uninvited.
I need them not, for what are these
  To one whose life is blighted?

They show me dishes rich and rare,
  But ah! my pulse no joy stirs.
For savouries I've ceased to care,
  I hate the thought of oysters.
They bring me roast, they bring me boiled,
  But all in vain they woo me;
The waiters softly mutter, 'Foiled!'
  The chef, poor man, looks gloomy.

So, EFFIE, turn that shell-like ear,
   Nor to my sighing close it,
You cannot doubt that I'm sincere—
   This ballad surely shows it.
No longer spurn the suit I press,
   Respect my agitation,
Do change your mind, and answer, 'Yes',
   And save me from starvation.

from Punch, 1901

THE POWER OF
GARLIC

HUMPHREY LYTTELTON

T WAS 1948 and my first working visit to France. On the esplanade at Nice, the day after the grand opening of the First International Jazz Festival at the Opera House, a fan dashed up, grabbed me by the shoulders and hit me full in the face with ''Amfree, last night you were *formidable*!' With the last syllable, he emptied his lungs and I went down like a felled ox. I was only unconscious for a second or two, but thought it wisest to stay down for the full count, lest he had taken the opportunity to reload.

Poor man, he meant well, and it is nice to know that, whatever may have happened to him since, he has at least lived a life immune from the ravages of arthritis, asthma, typhoid, wind, colics, obstructions of the kidney, spider's bite, consumption, intestinal worms, athletes' foot, embolism and the un-wanted attention of vampires. That immunity, according to the remarkably unanimous opinion of physicians and herbalists through the ages, derived from the lethal ingredients with which he had laced his lunch that afternoon in Nice. In a word, garlic.

Today, my vulnerability to his onslaught may seem strange. A rerun of the episode now would be a very different story, I can tell you. There's a Greek restaurant just down the road from my house which serves a delicious *hummous*, two spoonfuls of which, according to my family, would have sent my French enthusiast reeling *and* scorched the paint off every parked car within range. But the pre-war British fare on which I was brought up knew nothing of garlic, other than as just another unmentionable practice indulged in by unspeakable foreigners. No whiff of the stuff was permitted to permeate the pages of *Mrs Beeton's Cookery Book*, on which all well-bred eating, from country house lunches to public school dinners, was founded. Garlic was just another of the facts of life for which my expensive education left me ill-prepared.

Had the public school curriculum embraced herbalism among the other humanities, I would have emerged less ignorant. For while the noxious root was scorned for its gastronomic properties, it had for centuries been accepted as a cure-all. The herbalist Nicholas Culpeper asserted flatly in 1649 that 'the root is only known in physic', a view echoed over 300 years later by a modern practitioner, Dr Donald Law, who, in *Herbs for Cooking and for Healing*, introduced garlic as 'this strong-smelling medicine'.

Historical references to garlic-eating—they go back to, and beyond, the Egyptian pyramid-builders—almost all stress its medicinal properties. According to Aristophanes, Greek athletes used to take it to put themselves on their mettle in their exercises at the stadium. I don't know how the Olympics Committee would view that practice today, but at least its use would be easier to detect than that of steroids and other proscribed substances. According to Virgil, there was nothing like a clove or two of garlic to maintain the strength of the harvest reapers, while the Roman historian and naturalist Pliny went so far over the top as to claim that the smell of garlic 'drove off snakes and scorpions'.

And here, of course, we come back to the great snag about garlic. Stricken with any one of the ailments catalogued above, the sufferer is faced with a stark choice between losing his symptoms or losing his friends. To be fair, the herbalists have not dodged this issue. One of them, Bernadin de Saint-Pierre, said, 'Garlic, the smell of which is so dreaded by our little mistresses, is perhaps the most powerful remedy in existence against the vapours and nervous maladies to which they are subject.' Donald Law admits that 'the smell is somewhat overpowering', though he has little sympathy for shirkers.

'Some patients have foolishly refused Garlic on account of its smell and taste, but anybody who exhibits such behaviour is more in need of a psychologist than any other form of healer.'

I say, that's a bit hard! I would have thought that the quickest way to the funny farm, assuming the men in white coats could get near enough, would be to follow Dr Law's prescription of 'one to three cloves of Garlic eaten raw, and preferably chewed slowly' before venturing forth into polite society. It seems to be one of Providence's more unkind jokes, to equip us with an accessible and universal remedy and then attach to it such a prohibitive pong. Little wonder that much human endeavour and research have gone into tackling the problem over the centuries.

The most positive solution from the past is one that would no doubt commend itself to Dr Law. We are asked to believe that, taken in sufficient quantity, garlic will actually purify the breath! Don't laugh! There's a surprising witness to this theory in the shape of Ford Madox Ford, whom the great cookery pundit Elizabeth David calls in evidence to justify the quantity of garlic in some of her recipes.

He wrote, in 1938, of meeting at a party a ravishing French mannequin who was also a *cordon bleu* cook, lavish in her use of garlic. A thought occurred to him. 'Garlic is all very well on the bridge between Beaucaire and Tarascon or in the area at Nimes amongst sixteen thousand civilised beings . . . but in an *atelier de couture* in the neighbourhood of Hanover Square!' She explained to him, I hope less pompously than he reported, that 'the perfume of *allium officinale* attends only on those timorous creatures who have not the courage as it were to wallow in that vegetable'.

She hit on the solution by accident, it seems. Forced to resign her job by the complaints of her colleagues on the catwalks, she went home and consoled herself by cooking and eating a *Poulet Béarnais*, a dish that involves garnishing the chicken with no less than a kilo of garlic. Returning to the couturier's to collect her things, she was surprised to be met, not with muffled cries of protest, but with affectionate kisses and expressions of forgiveness. Says Ford Madox Ford, with rather unctuous satisfaction: 'She had solved the great problem. She had schooled her organs to assimilate, not to protest against, the sacred herb.'

Nowadays, with the health food boom once again emphasizing its therapeutic qualities, garlic is big business. Throughout the world, over two billion kilos of garlic a year are grown—enough for each of us to school our organs to the tune of half a clove a day. It may be that the French model's drastic action is no longer necessary. In 1982 the Japanese came up with a deodorized preparation which hit the jackpot in America. In Europe, we distil the oil from garlic by a steam process, put the result into gelatine capsules and swallow them by the million, confident that we are reaping the benefit without offending anyone. It's a far cry from our rustic ancestors'

38

recipe for treating a spider's bite with a cocktail of garlic, treacle and ale, or curing whooping cough by hobbling round with a clove of garlic in each shoe.

But does it work? The verdict of the medical scientists is that, so far as we know, Culpeper, Dr Law and the French model all have the edge over modern technology. Take away the smell, or dispatch it in gelatine to explode internally like some human underground nuclear test, and you lose most of the magic properties, too. So my advice is, if you feel the onset of catarrh or the fevers, come across a tarantula in that bunch of supermarket bananas, or hear the nocturnal flapping of webbed wings outside your bedroom window, to pop in a couple of cloves, chew slowly but resolutely— and hope to God that French lady was right . . .

from Highlife Magazine, June 1986

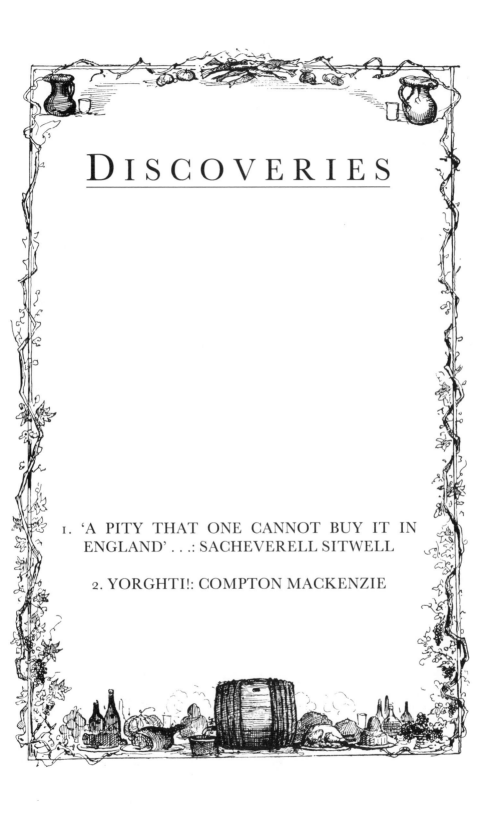

DISCOVERIES

'A PITY THAT ONE CANNOT BUY IT IN ENGLAND' ...

SACHEVERELL SITWELL

AMONG the delights of Portugal are the unfamiliar wines upon the wine lists. Particularly good are some of the light *vinhos verdes*, which belie their name and are more often red than the palish white which goes for green. But there is one wine that is altogether exceptional, and that comes from the remote northern province of Tras-os-Montes.

This is the most delicious *vin rosé* that I have ever tasted. It is called Mateus, and it may be that the view of the lovely villa of that name, near Vila Real, which is upon the label, makes the wine taste even better. For the villa has a façade of granite and white stucco, and many urns and statues. But what is unique in this wine is that it is the colour of orangeade, and slightly *pétillant*. Let no one despise it for its colour! Mateus is delicious beyond words; and since I am told that it will travel and is exported to Brazil, it is a pity that one cannot buy it here in England.

from The Sunday Times, 1951
[See Auberon Waugh, *My Father's Cellar*, p. 58]

YORGHTI!

COMPTON MACKENZIE

FOR some time after we went ashore we had no bread, and it was worth while learning by experience how detestable a meal can be without bread, for which biscuit is no sort of substitute. Yet after a couple of meals accompanied by bread the novelty wore off, and we were once again gazing distastefully at our plates. And then somebody who knew what he was talking about said that *Yorghti* was what we should be having every night. *Yorghti* is sour sheep's milk served in a bowl like junket, and the man who invented it should have as much respect as humanity has accorded to Prometheus. It may be discovered one day that Prometheus did invent it, and no doubt the gods were too much taken up with their own ambrosia to be jealous. *Yorghti!* And as I write the name of that substance I fain would sing with golden eloquence, I am conscious, remorsefully conscious, that I am probably not spelling it as it should be spelt. Somewhere on my shelves the orthography of that word must be hidden, but I cannot find it; and what does it matter? *Yorghti*, whatever way it may be spelt, is a ridiculous name for this life-giving stuff. At first, in the approved English fashion, the uninitiated members of the Mess turned up their noses at it. No doubt several sand-dried Israelites made an equivalent grimace of contempt over the first plate of manna put before them. Presently, however, everybody overcame his insular prejudice first against milking sheep at all and then against the deliberate turning of such unnatural milk sour, overcame his prejudice indeed so successfully that we at the junior end of the table began to look a little anxious as the bowl dallied unduly in the hands of our seniors. There was one older member of the Mess whose eyes used to glow like a lover's with real passion when the bowl reached him. This particular member was something of a puritan. I had often heard him speak in terms of unmeasured reprobation of men who had been willing to sacrifice their careers for women or wine or cards, and I was maliciously quick to note his own carnal weakness and point it out to others. Val Braithwaite and I used to bet with each other on the number of spoonfuls he would scoop on to his plate when the *yorghti* reached him; and once when X—— helped himself to nine generous spoonfuls, his eyes goggling in the candlelight, we derived so much enjoyment from the spectacle that we hardly minded having to scrape the bowl to find ourselves a meagre spoonful apiece. The whole case

43

of X—— and his greed over food interested me, because apart from that he was obviously a man of singularly ascetic habits, and his puritanism if betraying a little too much spiritual pride was unmistakably sincere and due to a real hatred of fleshly indulgence. Yet one might have fancied that he for a bowl of *yorghti* would have lapped away kingdoms and provinces even as once upon a time for Cleopatra Antony kissed them away.

from Gallipoli Memories, 1929

VARIATION ON A HORATIAN THEME

Persicos odi, puer, apparatus,
displicent nexae philyra coronae;
mitte sectari, rosa quo locorum
   sera moretur.

Boy, I detest the Persian style
Of elaboration. Garlands bore me
Laced up with lime-bark. Don't run a mile
   To find the last rose of summer for me.

simplici myrto nihil allabores
sedulus curo: neque te ministrum
dedecet myrtus neque me sub arta
   vite bibentem.

None of your fussy attempts to refine
On simple myrtle. Myrtle suits both
You pouring, me drinking, wine
   Under the trellised vine's thick growth.

Carminum Liber Primus: xxxviii

Odes: Book One: 38
James Michie: *The Odes of Horace*, 1964

AD MINISTRAM

Dear Lucy, you know what my wish is,—
   I hate all your Frenchified fuss:
Your silly entrées and made dishes
   Were never intended for us.
No footman in lace and in ruffles
   Need dangle behind my arm-chair;
And never mind seeking for truffles,
   Although they be ever so rare.

But a plain leg of mutton, my Lucy,
   I prithee get ready at three:
Have it smoking, and tender and juicy,
   And what better meat can there be?
And when it has feasted the master,
   'Twill amply suffice for the maid;
Meanwhile I will smoke my canaster,
   And tipple my ale in the shade.

W. M. Thackeray, 1850

SOME PEOPLE

HEMINGWAY AND WINE

STEFANO REGOLINI

RNEST HEMINGWAY, the most American of American writers, was enamoured of Europe. From this love arose two of his great passions: the bullfight and wine. Of the first, it must be immediately noted that what was involved was not simply a cruel sport, but a complex and fascinating ritual. In the book he dedicated to the sport, *Death in the Afternoon*, Hemingway explained that while there was an immediate attraction, in bullfighting as in all art the enjoyment increases with knowledge of the art.

The same is true of drinking wine, which the writer compared, precisely, with bullfighting. To the degree that a person's experience and his sensorial education grows, he can derive ever greater pleasure from wine, as the pleasure of a man at a *corrida* can increase so that it becomes one of his major infatuations.

The neophyte who goes to the arena for a bullfight is attracted by the picturesque *paseo*, the colours of the *farolas* and *molinetes*, by the romantic and commanding movements of the matador, who caresses the muzzle and horns of the bull, and by the tensions of the grandstand, before he comes to savour the elegance and languor of the *veronicas*, as Hemingway noted. He also observed that most men at the beginning prefer sweet wines, Sauternes, Barsac and fizzy wines like champagnes that are not too dry, or they bow before labels and before bottles that are dusty and covered with cobwebs. Only with time does the palate become more educated and capable of appreciating wine so that the joy and pleasure continue to grow. He recalled that in his youth all red wines with the exception of port seemed bitter to him and drinking consisted of throwing down enough to seem brave and tough.

It was in Italy that the writer learned that drinking wine can be transformed into a sort of sincere cult without becoming snobbish and more than a means of quenching thirst. Tocai and Valpolicella, which he found in the wineshops and country houses in the World War I period, introduced him to this new pleasure. And there was the Capri Bianco in a cup with peaches and strawberries that he drank at the Biffi in Milan in company with Agnes

48

von Kurowsky—the nurse Catherine Barkley in *Farewell to Arms*—while recovering from a wound in a leg.

Then, France and Paris of the postwar years, where the 'Lost Generation' passed its days and invented a new literature.

Little money but the will to live and talent to burn. And always wine. The strong output of Corsica, which was bought cheap at the Halles aux Vins and drunk while watching the fishermen along the Seine between the Ile-St.-Louis and the Place du Vert-Galant or at the races at Enghien, while eating bread and sausages. But if the occasion demanded it—a literary prize awarded to a friend or a good story finished—he would order Châteauneuf-du-Pape to accompany *tournedos sauce Béarnaise*.

Each bistrot and each café in Paris had for Hemingway the appeal of a certain dish and the odour of a certain wine. At the Nègre de Toulouse, there was the white of Cahors and truffled chicken. Oysters and dry white were the speciality at Place St.-Michel and there was calf's liver with puréed potatoes and endive salad consumed with Sancerre at Prunier.

On trips to the snows of Switzerland, a stop was always made at Sion for its wine and *truite au bleu*. On the way to Pamplona and its *fiesta*, a stop was made at Bresse for its chicken and the Montagneu. And he advised F. Scott Fitzgerald to drink the white of the Mâconnais, which was moderately fatty and with a low alcohol level, as a remedy for lung congestion. *A Movable Feast* is a book dedicated to Paris, to the writer's youth and also to the wines of France.

Death in the Afternoon is dedicated to bullfighting and to its violent atmosphere but also to the Spanish wines, of which Hemingway made a personal 'map'. He said that the best were those of the Bodegas Bilbainas, the Marqués de Murrieta and the Marqués de Riscal. Rioja Clarete or Rioja Alta are more pleasing and lighter red wines. Diamante is a good white wine for fish, Valdepeñas is a little less full than Rioja but it is excellent, whether white or red. The Spanish growers produced Chablis and Burgundy that he could not recommend. The Clarete Valdepeñas was an extremely good wine. The ordinary table wines of the environs of Valencia were quite good. Those of Tarragona were the best but travelled badly. Galicia had a good local ordinary table wine. For all those who went to Spain with sherry and Malaga in mind, he said, the magnificent light, dry reds would be a revelation. The ordinary table wine of Spain, he added, is decidedly superior to that of France, because it is not adulterated and the price is three times less.

At the Gritti or at Harry's Bar in Venice, where *Across the River and into the Trees* is set, the desperate and repeated words of Countess Renata and Colonel Cantwell float between toasts and sips of Capri Bianco and Val-policella in the fiasco or straw-wrapped bottle. The single exception is a Perrier-Jouet mentioned in the famous passage about the embrace on the gondola.

Hemingway's first and last love in matters of wine was, precisely, Val-policella. He said of it that it was best when it was young. It is not a great wine, he added, and to bottle and keep it for many years was only to accumulate a deposit. He kept a fiasco on the bedside table at the Villa Aprile in Cortina to help him wake up. Later, old and ailing, he had it shipped to him by sea at the Finca Vigia at Havana, paying an astronomical price for it and often seeing it arrive in disastrous state because of the sun and the travel. But he drank it until the doctors prohibited all alcohol.

Thirty years before, in *Death in the Afternoon*, a few lines after having written that wine is one of the best signs of civilization and one of the world's natural things brought to maximum perfection, he concluded that precisely when a character in the book had come to love it even more wine was forbidden him.

from Civilta del Bere, 1986

DUFF'S DRINKING
LIFE

JOHN JULIUS NORWICH

N your drinking life', my father said to me on my fifteenth birthday, 'there are only two liquids generally to be avoided. One is water, and the other is milk. The first gives you typhoid, the second tuberculosis. Stick to alcohol, which is Nature's first and best disinfectant, and you won't go very far wrong.' It was a philosophy which—apart from the bottle of Vichy water which he kept beside his bed every night of his peacetime life—he followed as conscientiously as he could; and although alcohol was, alas, forbidden to him for his last two years, he habitually answered all expressions of sympathy by pointing out that by the age of sixty he had already drunk far more good wine than most men drink in a lifetime and so hardly felt in a position to complain. Even then, he loved nothing better than to quote from the 'Heroic Poem in Praise of Wine' that his friend Hilaire Belloc had dedicated to him many years before:

> But what are these that from the outer murk
> Of dense mephitic vapours creeping lurk
> To breathe foul airs from that corrugated well
> Which oozes slime along the floor of Hell?
> These are the stricken palsied brood of sin
> In whose vile veins, poor, poisonous and thin,
> Decoctions of embittered hatreds crawl:
> These are the water-drinkers, cursed all!

Then the tone would change:

> For such as these in vain the Rhine has rolled
> Imperial centuries by hills of gold;
> For such as these the flashing Rhône shall rage
> In vain its lightning through the Hermitage,
> Or level-browed divine Touraine receive
> The tribute of her vintages at eve . . .
> Bootless for such as these the mighty task
> Of bottling God the Father in a flask
> And leading all Creation down distilled
> To one small ardent sphere immensely filled.

That was more like it. My father always saw wine—even the humblest of *vins ordinaires*—as a living being, a creature of moods and fancies, quirks and eccentricities just like the rest of us, but possessed also of some mystical, alchemical power capable of irradiating and transforming those who knew, cherished and understood it. He loved to tell of a rainy Sunday evening during the first world war when he had arrived unexpectedly in London from his camp at Bushey:

I could find nobody whom I knew in London. I went to dine alone at a club. A great cloud of depression came upon me and I felt even more miserable than I had been at Bushey and without hope.

It was one of those great station-hotels of clubs where I knew nobody, but where in those days the food was simple and good, and the wine very cheap. Also it had a library. I ordered an imperial pint of champagne, that admirable measure which like so many good things has disappeared from the world, and I took *Alice Through the Looking Glass* to accompany me during dinner. I wrote in my diary the next day: 'As by enchantment my melancholy left me and I knew that I should not be unhappy again. Courage came back to me which I had lost and I despised myself for having done so.' I went back to my flat, changed into my uniform, spoke to the Montagus who had just returned, and motored down to Bushey feeling perfectly happy.

For the last forty of his sixty-four years my father was a regular and faithful client of Berry Brothers; some of the most vivid of my teenage memories are of accompanying him to Number Three, St James's Street. The first record of wines bought by him from Berrys' goes back as far as July 1917—the time of the incident described above—when he paid 132/- for a case of 1904 Binet: an excellent vintage, I am told, from the shippers who still provide the firm with its house champagne, and—since it was already thirteen years old when purchased—a significant illustration of the way in which vintage champagne was at that time allowed to mature for considerably longer than it would normally be today.

In January 1926, by contrast, my father invested in two cases of 1924 Château Lafite only fifteen months after the vintage—an early example of buying *en primeur*, though whether he did so on advice or on the basis of a private hunch we shall never know. The wine was not delivered to my parents' house at 90 Gower Street for another six years, by which time it must have been well on the way to the distinction it was later to attain. To my eternal regret I never tasted any: I had been conceived and born in the interim, but by the time I grew old enough to enjoy it stocks had, I fear, long since been exhausted. A more familiar label to me—indeed, the first claret I ever tasted and the first château name I ever knew—was Château Beychevelle, of which my father bought no fewer than twenty four cases of the 1933 vintage (Berrys' having taken up the entire production) in January 1936, and had twenty of them sent down to our seaside house at Aldwick, near Bognor Regis. At 42/- a dozen it was a splendid buy; and I well remember how in the wartime summers of 1942 and 1943 it was still keeping us going. The ultimate jewel in our claret crown was, however, the 1906 Château Cheval Blanc, bought in November 1938. The price was 210/- a dozen: a lot of money in those days, particularly since the family fortunes were at a low ebb, my father having been out of a job since his resignation as First Lord of the Admiralty after the Munich agreement of two months before. He probably bought it to cheer him up; and—as the Cheval Blanc was apparently the star of an excellent, very long lasting vintage—I have no doubt that it did so.

Among the Burgundies, there was one particularly intriguing entry. I should dearly love to have seen—and tasted—the 1911 Musigny, which carried on its label the proud boast: 'Successfully concealed from the enemy during the German occupation of Liège, 1914–1918.' As for the Ports—of which my father seems to have bought, over the years, a quite alarming quantity—the *pièce de résistance* was the vintage of 1851, the year of the Great Exhibition. It too, one feels, must have had a good deal to show off; and the same could certainly have been said of the 1921 Château d'Yquem, for which he paid 252/- a dozen, or just a guinea a bottle: not bad, even then, for perhaps the finest dessert wine ever produced. The other star of the collection was a single bottle (as far as the records show) of 1837 Jubilee sherry: any single vintage sherry was, and is, extremely rare. We have, alas, no indication of how much he paid for it, and still less of when it was drunk; knowing the purchaser, however, I have little doubt that the occasion was worthy of the wine.

The records of my father's transactions with Berry Bros. throw a fascinating light on his tastes. I was delighted to see that already by 1938 he had discovered the beauties of Alsatian wine, of which in later years he was to become a passionate champion; and amused to see that in those days the wine was so little known in England that it was not allowed a designation of its own but was simply listed under 'Hock'. Seven years later my father was offering Sylvaner, Riesling and his favourite Gewürztraminer to guests at the Paris Embassy and, I suspect, doing much to make them popular in this country. After a year at the University of Strasbourg in 1946–47, I knew just how right he was.

By the 1930s, the cocktail age had reached its zenith; and I greatly enjoyed seeing, listed next to the '1809 Brandy (no label)', the sinister entry 'Gomme Sirop'. I have no idea what this may have been, but it sounds wonderfully nasty.* The list continues with such regular staples as 'Angostura Bitters (pint)'—which must have gone a long way—'Yellow Chartreuse (half-litre)' and 'Original Chartreuse (one-eighth litre)', the price of the latter being no less than 1260/- a case. My father always considered himself something of an expert on cocktails, and once won a competition in the *New Statesman* by producing an exotic recipe for one known as 'Sunshine', in the form of a sonnet:

> Rum, divine daughter of the sugar cane,
>   Rum, staunch ally of those who sail the sea,
>   Jamaican rum of rarest quality,
> One half of rum the goblet shall contain.
> Bring Andalusian oranges from Spain,
>   And lemons from the groves of Sicily,
>   Mingle their juice (proportions two to three)
> And sweeten all with Demeraran grain.
> Of Angosturan bitters just a hint,
>   And, for the bold, of brandy just a spice,
> A leaf or two of incense-bearing mint
>   And any quantity of clinking ice:
> Then shake, then pour, then quaff, and never stint,
>   Till life shall seem a dream of Paradise.

* Fruit juice preserved in gum arabic to sweeten long mixed drinks such as punches and cobblers. C.R.

He spent the prize money—supplemented, probably, by a considerable sum of his own—on a magnificent glass cocktail shaker from Fortnum and Mason, on which he had the sonnet engraved. It is, I am delighted to say, still in use.

After my father left the Paris Embassy at the end of 1947, he and my mother lived permanently in France—at the little Château de Saint-Firmin, just outside Chantilly—and Berry's consequently saw less of him, though he would usually drop in whenever he came to London. The most memorable of those occasions was the famous Rosebery Dinner, held in the dining room of Number Three on 26th January 1951. The point of the party was to provide a suitable occasion for Lord Rosebery to drink the pick of his cellar, most notably the 1864 and '65 Lafites. These wines were stored with the firm, and he understandably felt that they would be shown to their best advantage if they were decanted and served without being moved. He invited half the party, and Berry Brothers the other half; and the twelve lucky men—they included Lord Trent, Lord Rothschild, Eustace Hoare, Freddie Cripps, Murrough O'Brien and Lorne Campbell—sat down to enjoy some of the greatest wines that even they had ever tasted.

My father's own cellar was modest indeed compared to Lord Rosebery's; but it had meanwhile been shipped off *en bloc* to his new home, where it proved copious enough to see him through until his drinking days were done. Even then, however, when his own glass was never filled with anything stronger than ginger ale, he would regale his friends as generously as he ever had: and when, just a year before he died, he came to write his autobiography, *Old Men Forget*, he did not fail to record his thanks:

Writing in my sixty-fourth year, I can truthfully say that since I reached the age of discretion I have consistently drunk more than most people would say was good for me. Nor do I regret it. Wine has been to me a firm friend and wise counsellor. Often wine has shown me matters in their true perspective, and has, as though by the touch of a magic wand, reduced great disasters to small inconveniences. Wine has lit up for me the pages of literature, and revealed in life romance lurking in the commonplace. Wine has made me bold but not foolish; has induced me to say silly things but not to do them. Under its influence words have often come too easily which had better not have been spoken, and letters have been written which had better not have been sent. But if such small indiscretions standing in the debit column of wine's account were added up, they would amount to nothing in comparison with the vast accumulation on the credit side.

It is a fine tribute. Are there, I wonder, many readers of these words who would disagree with him?

from Number Three, St James's Street, House Magazine of Berry Bros. and Rudd, Autumn 1986/7

MY FATHER'S CELLAR

AUBERON WAUGH

FOR A MAN whose life revolved around wine, Evelyn Waugh wrote surprisingly little on the subject. Even his novels have few references to this lifelong passion, although there is a famous passage from *Brideshead Revisited*, when Charles Ryder, staying with his friend Sebastian, 'first made a serious acquaintance with wine and sowed the seed of that rich harvest which was to be my stay in many barren years'. Many will remember the scene when they sit up late in the Painted Parlour, getting their glasses more and more muddled as their praise for the wine grows wilder and more exotic:

'. . . It is a little shy wine like a gazelle.'
  'Like a leprechaun.'
  'Dappled, in a tapestry meadow.'
  'Like a flute by still water.'
  '. . . And this is a wise old wine.'
  'A prophet in a cave.'
  '. . . And this is a necklace of pearls on a white neck.'
  'Like a swan.'
  'Like the last unicorn . . .'
  'Ought we to be drunk *every* night?' Sebastian asked one morning.
  'Yes, I think so.'
  'I think so too.'

Goodness knows how many sottish late-night conversations that passage has inspired among later generations of Oxford undergraduates, but I feel it belongs among the immortal pieces of wine writing, along with Thurber's famous captions, from *Men, Women and Dogs*: 'It's a Naïve Domestic Burgundy, Without Any Breeding, But I Think You'll be Amused by its Presumption.'

One might also deduce from the scarcity of Evelyn Waugh's writing about wine that it belonged to that part of his life which he regarded as private. The fierceness with which he defended his own privacy gave rise to many of the stories—gossip columns were full of them—which portrayed him as a monstrous old blimp, roaring and yelling at any intruder into his private domain. In fact he was a gentle, humorous man—sometimes sad, sometimes

56

gloomy—and nowhere near as bad-tempered as he appeared to the Press and public on his few excursions outside the small world of family and friends. But I do not think it is betraying a trust to reveal an aspect of his private life which will be of great interest to wine-drinkers and which has never, so far as I know, been revealed before.

The mid-life crisis is familiar among males in our society. Many mark it by leaving their wives of many years and taking up with some luscious young dolly bird or, if they are not married (like Bernard Levin) they may give up their work and go to live at an *ashram* in Poona. Evelyn Waugh celebrated his own mid-life crisis first of all by going mad soon after his 50th birthday, in January 1954. This episode is well documented in his novel, *The Ordeal of Gilbert Pinfold*, first published in 1957 but available in Penguin. Next, having recovered his sanity, he sold his house and moved to the huge icebox at Combe Florey, in Somerset, where I now live. In the process, he suffered a violent change in his wine-drinking habits which was to remain with him for the rest of his life—he died in 1966—as the only permanent trauma from his experiences at this time. From that moment, he could *never touch a drop of claret*, in any circumstances.

It would be interesting to know if others have had the same experience in middle age. His house in Gloucestershire was famous for the excellence of its clarets—as for its vintage ports—but just before moving house, in the late autumn of 1956, he sold every bottle of claret in his cellar, and never bought another. Worse than this, he could not bring himself to drink any red wine from Bordeaux even in the house of friends. A year ago I found myself sitting next to Sir Hugh Greene, the former Director General of the BBC. Like the

Ancient Mariner, he held me with his skinny hand and told me a tale of woe which had understandably been haunting him for years. It appeared that at some time in the early 1960s, probably 1963, Evelyn Waugh had visited the BBC to make a broadcast about P. G. Wodehouse, and Greene had decided to give a dinner party at Broadcasting House. In Waugh's honour, Greene had procured rather a special bottle of claret—not just rather a special bottle, but the classic, never-to-be-forgotten Cheval Blanc 1947. Evelyn Waugh thanked him very much, but declined to take any. End of story.

Plainly, this violent repudiation of the world's second best wine-producing area was the result of some psychological trauma, if not actual brain damage. He was quite happy to experiment with wines from unlikely places like Chile (probably of Cabernet base, although in those days they did not specify the grape) and once discovered a new enthusiasm for the red wines of Germany. Even more shaming than that, he came back from Rhodesia one day announcing a new discovery from Portugal called Mateus Rosé, and drank it through one whole summer. Whenever challenged with this, I loyally maintain that the Mateus Rosé of the late '50s was a quite different wine from the sugary pink fizz of today, but I do not honestly know where the truth lies.*

At any rate, no claret ever entered the cellar at Combe Florey until 1971, when I moved back. At Evelyn Waugh's death in 1966 he left four or five dozen Chambertin 1955 from Berry Bros.—a magnificent wine, but one which would have improved with keeping in less frigid surroundings than the cellars at Combe Florey. Although, so far as I know, no wine has ever actually frozen solid down there, I cannot think why not, as the temperature in his day was frequently below freezing point. He also had two cases of Richebourg from Berrys'—I think the vintage was also 1955—some odd parcels of rather old Sauternes, notably Suduiraut 1947, and a lot of champagne, notably Clicquot Rosé for which he had developed an old man's passion. There were no bottles of vintage port and nothing else.

I think I may have one clue, which is neither psychological nor bio-chemical, for Evelyn Waugh's repudiation of claret. For some reason, he always referred to it as 'clart', even in such homely expressions as 'to tap the claret', meaning to draw blood in a fight. 'Have a glass of clart,' he would say. Some had difficulty in understanding what he meant, but he persisted. Then in 1956 there was published a rather shameful book called *Noblesse Oblige*, edited by Nancy Mitford, with contributions from herself, Waugh, John Betjeman, Christopher Sykes and others, discussing the characteristics of the English upper class. In the course of his contribution, Sykes—who was

---

* See Sacheverell Sitwell's 'Discovery' of Mateus Rosé, which must have been before 1951, p. 42.

a friend of my father's, despite being, as he frequently pointed out, of better breeding—mentioned 'a Gloucestershire landowner' who believed 'that persons of family always refer to the wines of Bordeaux as "clart", to rhyme with cart' Mr Sykes opined that 'this delusion' showed 'an impulse towards gentility' which might be preferable to the contrary impulse, among true aristocrats, towards affecting the mannerisms of the proletariat.

My father spotted the reference to himself immediately, and although he took it in good part, it must have left him in something of a quandary. Either he had to drop his harmless affectation in deference to the mockery of a younger man and lesser artist, which he did not deign to do, or he had to persist in the awareness that everyone was sniggering at him as the Gloucestershire landowner who said 'clart' when he meant 'claret'. I do not know how much influence it had on his subsequent behaviour, but it is a fact that within a year he had sold not only his house in Gloucestershire but also all his claret, and never touched the stuff again.

I cannot leave the subject without touching on Evelyn Waugh's wine-writing such as it was. His main contribution to the field (I exclude his work on a history of Veuve Clicquot) was a booklet called *Wine in Peace and War* published by Saccone and Speed in 1947. It has never been reprinted, and has little of contemporary relevance in it. I observe from his correspondence with his agent, A. D. Peters, that he was paid at the rate of 12 bottles of champagne per 1000 words—not an immensely generous rate, I would say. Perhaps that explains why he wrote so little on the subject. I am sure he could have done better.

The last thing he wrote about wine appeared in the New York *Vogue* in the year before he died. It dealt with champagne, and described the circumstances in which it should be drunk: 'For two intimates, lovers or comrades, to spend a quiet evening with a magnum, drinking no apéritif before, nothing but a glass of cognac after—that is the ideal . . . The worst time is that dictated by convention, in a crowd, in the early afternoon, at a wedding reception.'

That comment strikes me as profoundly true. Immense harm is done to champagne by the English habit of drinking it, usually warm and in a sort of trifle dish, at weddings in the early afternoon. That is why so many people in England claim to dislike champagne.

An even profounder claim is made in the first writing I have been able to trace by him in the December 1937 issue of *Harper's Bazaar*, under the title 'Laying Down a Wine Cellar.'

'Wine lives and dies; it has not only its hot youth, strong maturity and weary dotage, but also its seasonal changes, its mysterious, almost mystical, link with its parent vine, so that when the sap is running in the wood on the middle slopes of the Côte d'Or, in a thousand cellars a thousand miles away the wine in its bottle quickens and responds.'

I wonder if there is any truth in this theory. We have all noticed extraordinary variations from bottle to bottle within a matter of a month or two but I have never thought of relating them to seasonal changes in Burgundy, Bordeaux, the Lebanon or wherever. Perhaps it is true that many wines—not ports nor old-fashioned 'cooked' Burgundies—go to sleep in the winter. If this is true, we should drink Australian, South African and Chilean wine throughout the winter, French wine only in the spring and summer months. California wines, by the same token, can be drunk all the year round.

Or perhaps it is all a load of codswallop. I was never entirely convinced that my father, for all his poetic gifts, knew very much about wine. Certainly his brother, Alec, knew much more. When Evelyn wrote those words, he was just laying down his first cellar. My grandfather, Arthur Waugh, who was a publisher and critic, drank nothing but Keystone Australian Burgundy, a beverage which he believed to have tonic properties, much to the embarrassment of his two sons.

Even so, my father, who wrote in 1937 that 'nothing is easier than to ruin a fine wine by careless handling,' was among the worst offenders in this respect. He never brought up a wine to the dining room more than half an hour before a meal—not that it would have made much difference if he had, as the dining room was nearly as cold as the cellar; and he never opened a bottle before it was time to drink it. In his last years he drank splendid burgundy, day after day, at temperatures which many would judge too cold for Sauternes.

But the saddest part of the article, written as a young man of 33, concerns ports of a great vintage: 'it is at least fifteen years before they become drinkable, and fifty before they are at their prime; some superlative vintages will live a century. It is these vintages which one should buy as soon as they are shipped and lay securely down for one's old age, or for posterity.'

Perhaps he had rather lost his enthusiasm for posterity by the time he died, at the sadly young age of 62. Despite his golden opportunity to lay down the 1963 vintage before his death in 1966, he left no port at all.

from Number Three, St James's Street, House Magazine of
Berry Bros. and Rudd, Spring 1986

THE PALMER OF
CHATEAU PALMER

HOWELL REES GRONOW

ENERAL PALMER. This excellent man had the last days of his life embittered by the money-lenders. He had commenced his career surrounded by every circumstance that could render existence agreeable; fortune, in his early days, having smiled most benignantly on him. His father was a man of considerable ability, and was to the past generation what Rowland Hill is in the present day—the great benefactor of correspondents. He first proposed and carried out the mail-coach system; and letters, instead of being at the mercy of postboys, and a private speculation in many instances, became the care of Government, and were transmitted under its immediate direction.

*   *   *

Mr Palmer was successful in his undertaking, and at his death his son found himself the inheritor of a handsome fortune, and became a universal favourite in Bath.

The corporation of that city, consisting of thirty apothecaries, were, in those borough-mongering days, the sole electors to the House of Commons, and finding young Palmer hospitable, and intimate with the Marquis of Bath and Lord Camden, and likewise desiring for themselves and their families free access to the most agreeable theatre in England,* they returned him to Parliament. He entered the army, and became a conspicuous officer in the 10th Hussars, which regiment being commanded by the Prince Regent, Palmer was at once introduced at Carlton House, the Pavilion at Brighton, and consequently into the highest society of the country; for which his agreeable manners, his amiable disposition, and his attainments, admirably qualified him. His fortune was sufficiently large for all his wants; but, unfortunately, as it turned out, the House of Commons voted to him, as the representative of his father, £100,000, which he was desirous of laying out to advantage.

A fine opportunity, as he imagined, had presented itself to him; for, in

---

* The Theatre Royal, Bath, owned by Palmer's father, burned down 1862, later rebuilt. C.R.

61

travelling in the diligence from Lyons to Paris—a journey then requiring three days—he met a charming widow, who told a tale that had not only a wonderful effect upon his susceptible heart, but upon his amply-filled purse. She said her husband, who had been the proprietor of one of the finest estates in the neighbourhood of Bordeaux, was just dead, and that she was on her way to Paris to sell the property, that it might be divided, according to the laws of France, amongst the family. Owing, however, to the absolute necessity of forcing a sale, that which was worth an enormous sum would realise one quarter only of its value. She described the property as one admirably fitted for the production of wine; that it was, in fact, the next estate to the Château Lafitte,* and would prove a fortune to any capitalist. The fascinations of this lady, and the temptation of enormous gain to the speculator, impelled the gallant colonel to offer his services to relieve her from her embarrassment; so by the time the diligence arrived in Paris he had become the proprietor of a fine domain, which was soon irrevocably fixed on him by the lady's notary, in return for a large sum of money: and, had the colonel proved a man of business, he would no doubt have been amply repaid, and his investment might have become the source of great wealth.

Palmer, however, conscious of his inaptitude for business, looked around him for an active agent, and believed he had found one in a Mr Gray, a man of captivating manners and good connections, but almost as useless a person as the general himself. Fully confident in his own abilities, Gray had already been concerned in many speculations; but not one of them had ever succeeded, and all had led to the demolition of large fortunes. Plausible in his address, and possessing many of those superficial qualities that please the multitude, he appeared to be able to secure for the claret—which was the production of the estate—a large *clientèle*. Palmer's claret, under his auspices, began to be talked of in the clubs; and the *bon vivant* was anxious to secure a quantity of this highly-prized wine.

The patronage of the Prince Regent being considered essential, was solicited, and the prince, with his egotistical good-nature, and from a kindly feeling for Palmer, gave a dinner at Carlton House, when a fair trial was to be given to his claret. A select circle of *gastronomes* was to be present, amongst whom was Lord Yarmouth, well known in those days by the appellation of 'Red-herrings', from his rubicund whiskers, hair, and face, and from the town of Yarmouth deriving its principal support from the importation from Holland of that fish; Sir Benjamin Bloomfield, Sir William Knighton, and Sir Thomas Tyrwhitt, were also of the party. The wine was produced, and was found excellent, and the spirits of the party ran high; the light wine animating them without intoxication. The Prince was delighted, and, as usual upon such occasions, told some of his best stories, quoted Shakespeare,

---

* *Sic.* C.R.

and was particularly happy upon the bouquet of the wine as suited 'to the holy Palmer's kiss'.

Lord Yarmouth alone sat in a moody silence, and, on being questioned as to the cause, replied that whenever he dined at his Royal Highness's table, he drank a claret which he much preferred—that which was furnished by Carbonell. The prince immediately ordered a bottle of this wine; and to give them an opportunity of testing the difference, he desired that some anchovy sandwiches should be served up. Carbonell's wine was placed upon the table: it was a claret made expressly for the London market, well dashed with Hermitage,* and infinitely more to the taste of the Englishmen than the delicately-flavoured wine they had been drinking. The banquet terminated in the prince declaring his own wine superior to that of Palmer's, and suggesting that he should try some experiments on his estate to obtain a better wine. Palmer came from Carlton House much mortified. On Sir Thomas Tyrwhitt

---

* A. L. Henderson, *History of Ancient and Modern Wines* (1824). 'There is even a particular manufacture, called *Travail à l'Anglaise*, which consists in adding to each hogshead of Bordeaux three or four gallons of Alicante or Benicarlo, half a gallon of stum wine [unfermented grape juice] and sometimes a small quantity of hermitage . . . it is exported under the name of CLARET.' C.R.

attempting to console him, and saying that it was the anchovies that had spoiled the taste of the connoisseurs, the general said, loudly enough to be heard by Lord Yarmouth, 'No; it was the confounded red herrings.' A duel was very nearly the consequence.

General Palmer, feeling it his duty to follow the advice of the prince, rooted out his old vines, planted new ones, and tried all sorts of experiments at an immense cost, but with little or no result. He and his agent, in consequence, got themselves into all sorts of difficulties, mortgaged the property, borrowed largely, and were at last obliged to have recourse to usurers, to life assurances, and every sort of expedient, to raise money. The theatre at Bath was sold, the Reform in Parliament robbed him of his seat, and at last he and his agent became ruined men. A subscription would have been raised to relieve him, but he preferred ending his days in poverty to living upon the bounty of his friends. He sold his commission, and was plunged in the deepest distress; while the accumulation of debt to the usurers became so heavy, that he was compelled to pass through the Insolvent Court.

Thus ended the career of a man who had been courted in society, idolised in the army, and figured as a legislator for many years. His friends, of course, fell off, and he was to be seen a mendicant in the streets of London—shunned where he once was courted. Gray, his agent, became equally involved; but, marrying a widow with some money, he was enabled to make a better fight. Eventually, however, he became a prey to the money-lenders, and his life ended under circumstances distressing to those who had known him in early days.

from Captain Gronow, *Recollections, 3rd series*, 1865

NOSTALGIA

ANTHONY BURGESS

M Y GRANDFATHER Jack Wilson, kept a pub in north-east Manchester called the Derby Inn. There was a nominal irony in his being a Catholic landlord. He followed the tradition of having an Irish wife—Mary Ann Finnegan from Tipperary. He had a large appetite for traditional Lancashire dishes—hotpot, steak and cowheel pie, Eccles cakes, black puddings. He was pointed at in the street as the man who could 'ate a tater pie as big as his yed'. I was brought up on the same diet, though I have always found black puddings (balls of fat and blood polished with oil) far too rich for a naturally weak stomach.

Some years ago, in a *Paris Review* interview, I gave my American interlocutor the recipe for Lancashire hotpot. The dish is made of alternating layers of trimmed best end of neck of mutton with sliced onions and potatoes in a large earthenware dish. Stock is added, and finally oysters. The whole is cooked slowly in an oven and eaten with pickled red cabbage. It was a favourite dish on New Year's Eve in Lancashire Catholic households—or rather it was taken out of the oven just before the striking of midnight. New Year's Eve, preceding as it does the Feast of the Circumcision, used to be a day of abstinence. To rush to eat meat as soon as the vigil was over was seen as a jocular flirting with sin, and the New Year hotpot was called the Devil's Supper.

I have, in the long voyage from childhood to a kind of retirement in a Catholic principality (a sort of homing, really), tackled most of the cuisines of the world, but, as Lin Yu Tang said, we are finally loyal to the food of our youth, and this is perhaps what patriotism means. In exile I can cook dishes like hotpot, meat and potato pie, steak pie with cowheel (a Bolton speciality, as Jeanne Moreau, who has Bolton blood, reminded me). I cannot get Eccles cakes, nor the pork sausages sold by Seymour Meads on Princess Road, Manchester.

from Little Wilson and Big God, 1987

POET'S PICNIC

JOHN FULLER

I N T H E dry instructions to one of his dry pieces, Poulenc tells his pianist to have a glass of brandy on top of the piano. Excellent advice! Often, when I'm at the keyboard, I extend it to other works of his, particularly the clarinet sonata (though that is pretty hard on the clarinettist, whose mouth is involved elsewhere). There is a mysterious affinity between alcohol and art nowhere better illustrated than in the inspirational effect of an inch or two to hand when you sit down to write. The doyen of all bibulous poets is Dr William King of whom Johnson said he 'would write verses in a tavern three hours after he could not speak'. In summer I leave Oxford for Wales, leave, that is to say, serious drinking for serious writing. At a college feast one may sniff the fairy châteaux of the Médoc, whose strange hyphenated names buzz in the vinous memory like bees in the flowers of Eden. At the college wine society they may discuss Beaune as earnestly as the proposals of a great philosopher. But in Wales it is all Spar and hedgerow, a matter of scavenging, inspiration and the greater blessing of well-being. A white Lambrusco at £1.89 may be shot through the knees with antifreeze, but it may be about all you can get. Fear not: Pope, adapting Horace, wrote, 'The pleasure lies in you and not the meat.' Give a grouch Chassagne-Montrachet and it will taste grouchy; take the Lambrusco to your garden hammock and it will do very nicely. The extemporised practicalities of summer drinking are perfectly adapted to one's fitness and good intentions. The notebook fills as the bottle empties.

If your bottles are not to hand when the drinking hour arrives, it's no good walking the mile into the village, since its only shop sells little more than Corona, and pubs are to be avoided in the summer. (Perhaps poets should avoid pubs at all times, since beer tempts to a windy excess. It is no accident that Dylan Thomas's very name is an anagram of 'O malt shandy!') Real thirst is better slaked with the season's natural offerings, when being prepared is an urgent matter of exploiting their passing presence. Perfect after a long August walk, your elderflower cordial must be made in June. April gorse wine will be ready in September. Bramble wine must be made *the previous year*. If you are not prepared, you must make do with Welsh water, but even that is good enough to bottle.

The Pope/Horace principle allows a terrific amount of virtuous hill-walking followed by any practically nameless red wine. Even if all you can really taste is a sort of rootiness reaching for a thin soil, it will taste much better than an expensive classed growth taken in corpulence. Keats was young enough to swig *his* red bubbly (perhaps it was a red Lambrusco?) immobile in a deckchair in St John's Wood, blackening the paper with admiration of the nightingale. He was asking for trouble, though. Much better to take your two-litre plastic bottle to beach picnics, sweating to gather driftwood. The bottle will shrivel to a blister in the fire, while in its glow odes spring unbidden to the pen, and you can go swimming after sunset.

It is festive to drink cocktails, but fatal to start too soon, or go on too long. The groundwork of your sonnet can be laid in twenty minutes, and you can almost make the first drink last that long. Your best lines occur to you just after someone has proposed making a second round. But after three glasses you are fit for nothing but Verse Consequences, all giggles and smut.

This reduces the need for a variety of bottles, and lends the summer its particular character. Last year we drank Old-Fashioneds, the year before that Manhattans, the year before that Scholeses (my own invention, white rum and dry Dubonnet, named for Isabel Scholes, whose personal characteristics the drink attempted to approximate). What will it be in 1986? I'm tempted by something up-market like Kir Royale—champagne and mulberry cassis (I always find the ordinary kind too reminiscent of Ribena)—but I suppose that isn't appropriate to Wales. But whatever is? We once tried Sheep-Dip (gin, sherry and cider) but even the midges avoided it. Perhaps I shall make Icebergs (vodka and pastis).

It is well known that it rains a great deal in Wales, and therefore at this point the Woolcott Principle comes in ('I must just get out of these wet clothes and into a Dry Martini': Alexander Woolcott). Beware! Previous rules have applied to alfresco drinking, when the rockiest cocktail proves to have surprisingly limp wrists. When the weather keeps you indoors it is as well to be virtuous. I recommend something lighter, like a pink tonic or a spritzer. You can thus drink more *and* write more. If you need to feel that you're actually drinking something more interesting you could put a slice of lemon in it, but I really prefer my wine unadulterated. New Orleans must be the only 'French' city in the world where you can be served a glass of Chablis with an apple segment stuck on the rim of the glass. I suppose Keats could have made something of that, sensation-seeker that he was. Come to think of it, he could just about have drunk cocktails if he'd been American. The big question is, would he have stuck to three glasses?

from Harper's and Queen Magazine, May 1986

DOWN UNDER, FROM UP HERE

PAUL LEVY

NTIL a couple of years ago I was rather snobby (and silly) about Australian wine. The whites, I was convinced, were flabby, and dull; the reds I believed to be rough and over-alcoholic. Now every wine-drinker knows how wrong I was. Thanks to the weakness of the Australian dollar (or the strength of the pound), we have become an important enough export market for Oz to have flooded us with some of their best wines.

Oddbins have this year featured over 30 Aussie labels at sensationally good prices, and a specialist wine merchant such as Ostlers, in London, stocks a range that would more than stretch a marsupial's pouch. The supermarkets have caught on too.

Australian winemakers no longer bother to pretend that what they are doing has any relation to French or European winemaking. In the early days they called their wines burgundy, chablis, claret, anything they liked, as long as it corresponded to the colour of the European wine whose name was being taken in vain. Now they use almost exclusively varietal names, with the great grape types being chardonnay, rhine riesling, semillon and, increasingly, sauvignon blanc for the whites, cabernet sauvignon and shiraz (which the EEC is going to force them to label syrah). Pinot noir is difficult to grow and vinify successfully. The biggest selling white, from Houghton's in Western Australia—the wine that provided most Aussie wine drinkers with the occasion of their conversion from beer—is still, misleadingly, referred to as 'white burgundy'; but nowadays, no one is actually deceived. Most of the grapes, in any case, take on very different characteristics when grown in the Australian soil and climate.

The cabernets mature more rapidly than in France, and the shiraz produces a powerfully fruity wine with little of the austere discipline exhibited by that variety when grown in the northern Rhône. Chardonnay also makes unusually potent wine in Oz. Australia still makes some dessert wines—the muscat grape flourishes as does that strange variety the orange muscat. Fortified wines, like Galway Pipe, are still made too.

And being in the southern hemisphere has definite advantages from a marketing point of view. The vintage being six months in advance of ours, and the wine quicker to mature, Oz nouveau is always the first on the shelf, and often the most amusing. It seems amazing, at first, that all the vineyards are in the southern third of the country—with the best areas being the Margaret River in Western Australia, plus the many wine-growing areas of Southern Australia, much of the southernmost states of Victoria and Tasmania, and the Hunter Valley of New South Wales—until you reflect that those are the areas *furthest* from the Equator.

from Observer Colour Magazine, 13 October 1987

DOWN UNDER DITTY

B. A. YOUNG

Once a jolly swagman camped by a billabong,
 Under the shade of a Cabernet vine,
And he sang as he dragged the bottles from his tucker-bag
 Who'll come a-drinking Australian wine?
 Drinking Kooninga! Drinking Barossa!
  Drinking Milawa if that's what you choose!
 All you choosy oenophiles, bored with all that Beaujolais,
  Who'll come a-drinking Australian booze?

See the clever swagman quartering the continent,
 Walking the songlines from Brisbane to Perth,
Mustering the emus to rob them of their trademarks
 He hopes we'll be seeing all over the earth!

Imagining the vineyards from Innisfail to Bunbury
 Sprouting on the ranges all around,
With Shiraz and Sauvignon, Semillon and Chardonnay,
 Never a grape that wouldn't abound.

Then there'd be the shelves in every Aussie winestore,
 What a selection he thinks he sees
Of case after case of antipodean vintages,
 All bearing labels as splendid as these:

Wallumbilla, Birdum, Yilliminning, Walleroo,
   Yamma Yamma, Wollongong, Alice Springs,
Oodnadatta, Morrambidgee, Banka Banka, Booligal,
   And scads of other delectable things.

Down came a wine-merchant. He said, 'Listen, cobber,
   'They may sound pretty, but they're not quite right.
'When you hear the punters dining with their sheilas,
   'They ask for something easy, like plain Dry White.

'We're as keen as you are on your patriotic wine-list,
   'We just have to argue on the grounds
'That you can't plant a vineyard just for the name of it,
   'So let's go a-drinking some easier sounds.
     'Drinking McWilliam's! Drinking Rosemount!
      'Drinking Penfolds Bin 389!
    'You'll find the geography is only in the small print
     'When you're a-choosing Australian wine.'

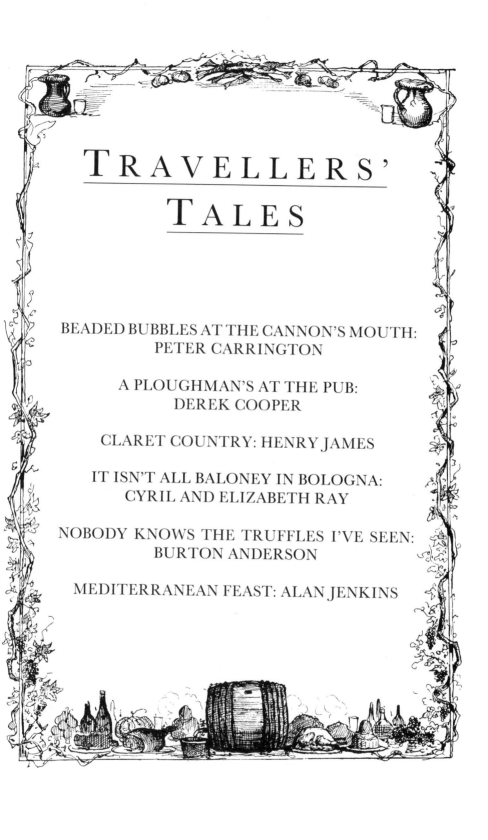

TRAVELLERS' TALES

BEADED BUBBLES AT THE CANNON'S MOUTH

PETER CARRINGTON

IN WAR time one of the more convenient aspects of serving in a tank battalion rather than an infantry battalion is the ability to carry more of your personal possessions with you. There is a limit to what can be carried on one's back, and uncertainty as to if and when and how the wheeled transport will catch up with you. This was very forcibly brought home to me in 1944 when I used to see my colleagues in the infantry, cold, wet and tired, digging a hole for themselves in which to spend the night whilst we dug a shallow trench, ran the tank over it and spent a warm, comfortable and safe night surrounded, if not by the creature comforts to which we have all become accustomed in later years, at any rate by much less discomfort than my foot-slogging friends. In September 1944 I discovered another and yet more important advantage.

The Guards Armoured Division entered Brussels on 3 September to much rejoicing by the population, a welcome which was certainly not matched anywhere else we went. The people of Brussels stormed our tanks, fifty or sixty standing or sitting on each vehicle. Flags, champagne, the lot—it was a riot. Eventually we moved on to spend the night outside the gates of the Royal Palace at Laeken. Providentially (and genuinely) on that very night my tank broke down and, whilst my squadron moved on, for the next 48 hours I remained behind in Brussels. The following day, accompanied by a brother officer, I was told by a friendly and far-seeing Belgian that not far away in a railway goods yard just outside Brussels was a large warehouse used to store the wine of the entire German army on the Western front. On arrival we discovered a shed of vast proportions filled to the roof with brandy, champagne, claret and burgundy. Not wishing to appear too selfish we felt it right to inform not only our battalion but also divisional headquarters of this agreeable discovery.

Within the space of a few hours all unwarlike stores had been unloaded from every three-ton lorry and a queue of trucks were loading champagne and brandy for the various regiments and battalions of the division. For myself I decided that probably the claret and the burgundy would not travel very well. I therefore appropriated twenty cases of champagne and loading them with considerable

76

difficulty into my jeep set off back to my tank. Those of you who are familiar with a Sherman tank, and I hope for your sake that that is a very small number, will know that the five large Chrysler engines which powered it were to be found under the flat space at the back. My champagne was firmly strapped down and off we went back to the war, opening a bottle now and again as we lay in comfort and security in our shallow trench under the tank, entertaining occasionally a passing infantryman who eyed my cellar with understandable envy. It must be admitted that it was not very good champagne. It must equally be acknowledged that having been shaken up all day (a Sherman is no limousine) and lying on the equivalent of a red hot Aga did not do too much to improve it. But we were not so sophisticated in those days and it was better than army tea.

The twenty cases did not last all that long. I drank the last bottle with Chester Wilmot (the war correspondent) at Nijmegen a month or so later. He didn't seem to me to appreciate either the quality of what he was offered or the fact that it was my last bottle.* What happened to the rest of that wine in the goods yard in Brussels? It was taken over by the NAAFI and sold back to us at what in 1944 seemed to us the vast sum of a pound a bottle . . .

---

*I was waiting at Nijmegen with the U.S. 82nd Airbourne Division for Captain Lord Carrington to arrive with the Guards Armoured. My old colleague Chester might have had the decency to leave me that bottle . . . C.R.

A PLOUGHMAN'S AT THE PUB

DEREK COOPER

THERE are few things more pleasurable than conversing with an informed enthusiast. Last Monday I went down to Selborne to record an interview for the *Meridian* book programme with Richard Mabey, who has just written a biography of the village's most famous son, Gilbert White. Apart from hovering army Chinooks and a Sainsbury's van which hurtled past the Wakes where Gilbert lived and nearly pinned me to the wall, little seems to have changed in this idyllic part of England for a couple of centuries. We chatted under the shadow of a yew which has been growing in the churchyard for over 1,200 years and after an active morning decided we needed a pint. Richard took me to a nearby village, where we had some Badger's bitter brewed in Dorset, as perfect an ale as ever I drank. With it, in this one-time haunt of honest ploughmen, we had a snack which in pub circles is referred to as a 'Ploughman's'. The snow-white bread was like lint; the cheddar unmatured and soapy; there were three onions which appeared to have been pickled in acetic acid and a token slice or two of tasteless tomato. We have the scenery in England, we have the history and the heritage. I wish we cared a bit more about the food . . .

from The Listener, 26.vi.86

CLARET COUNTRY

HENRY JAMES

BORDEAUX gives a great impression of prosperous industries, and suggests delightful ideas, images of prune-boxes and bottled claret. As the focus of distribution of the best wine in the world, it is indeed a sacred city—dedicated to the worship of Bacchus in the most discreet form. The country all about it is covered with precious vineyards, sources of fortune to their owners and of satisfaction to distant consumers; and as you look over to the hills beyond the Garonne you see them in the autumn sunshine, fretted with the rusty richness of this or that immortal *clos*. But the principal picture, within the town, is that of the vast curving quays, bordered with houses that look like the *hôtels* of farmers-general of the last century, and of the wide, tawny river, crowded with

shipping and spanned by the largest of bridges. Some of the types on the waterside are of the sort that arrest a sketcher—figures of stalwart, brown-faced Basques, such as I had seen of old in great numbers at Biarritz, with their loose circular caps, their white sandals, their air of walking for a wager.

Never was a tougher, a harder race. They are not mariners, nor watermen but, putting questions of temper aside, they are the best possible dock-porters. 'Il s'y fait un commerce terrible', a *douanier* said to me, as he looked up and down the interminable docks; and such a place has indeed much to say of the wealth, the capacity for production, of France—the bright, cheerful, smokeless industry of the wonderful country which produces, above all, the agreeable things of life, and turns even its defeats and revolutions into gold. The whole town has an air of almost depressing opulence, an appear-ance which culminates in the great *place* which surrounds the Grand-Théâtre—an establishment in the highest style, encircled with columns, arcades, lamps, gilded cafés. One feels it to be a monument to the virtue of the well-selected bottle. If I had not forbidden myself to linger, I should venture to insist on this, and, at the risk of being considered fantastic, trace an analogy between good claret and the best qualities of the French mind; pretend that there is a taste of sound Bordeaux in all the happiest manifesta-tions of that fine organ, and that, correspondingly, there is a touch of French reason, French completeness, in a glass of Pontet-Canet.

from A Little Tour in France, 1884

BORDELAY

The girls of Bordeaux, I'm afraid,
You would hardly consider as *staid*:
A young Bordelaise
Knows of *dozens* of ways
In which she can get bordelaide . . .

from Lickerish Limericks

IT ISN'T ALL
BALONEY
IN BOLOGNA

CYRIL AND ELIZABETH RAY

So FAMOUS for so long for so many different kinds of sausage, Bologna has given its name to polony and, by unfair extension, to what the *OED* defines as 'humbug, nonsense'. But it doesn't matter how you slice it, Bologna is still the heart and soul of Emilia-Romagna, a bounteous region renowned for much else—not least for forming a pasta-making, pasta-cooking and pasta-enjoying salient jutting northwards into regions where Venetians, Lombards and such eat polenta (made from maize) and rice.

As for the pasta country to the south, they shake their pitying heads here over the poor Neapolitans—'Can't afford meat, so they smother their stringy stuff with tomato sauce, whereas we twist our pasta into fanciful little pockets' (some fashioned, they say, after Venus's navel) and stuff them with beef and pork and veal, or cheese and spinach, or a pumpkin or a chestnut filling. Pasta incapable of being stuffed, such as *tagliatelle* (not Venus's navel, this one, but Lucrezia Borgia's hair), they serve with what lesser breeds call a bolognese sauce, but called here *ragù*, made with beef and bacon and chicken-livers and butter and vegetables and herbs and red wine and garlic and stock: '*Spaghetti bolognese*? Never heard of it.'

In a tiny *osteria* open of an evening behind a bar named, for some odd reason, Le Fiacre, in the Via Irnerio, Ronaldo explained the combinations and permutations that could be made of its dozen kinds of pasta with twice as many sauces. We made *tortellini* our main course, stuffed and garnished and sauced with baby globe artichokes which, with house wine before and during, the freshest and most generous of fruit salads, coffee and a brandy, totted up to about £17 for the two of us.

Where there are students these days, alas, there is junk food, and Bologna's is the oldest university in Europe, but there are far fewer hamburgers and cans of Coke here than in any European city of its size: more typical is Ragù, Piazza VIII Agosto, quickly serving hot dishes of the day, as well as pasta, salads and deliciously moist, coarse-cut, spicy bangers, from about £1.50 to £4 a dish, all in, and house wine in half-litres at 50p.

A sight for sore eyes, sometimes in that piazza, sometimes in others, is a peripatetic covered stall displaying a whole roast sucking-pig from which sandwiches are served at about £2 a time. A Bolognese friend, too proud of his own city's cuisine to take credit for another's, said, 'Ah, yes, delicious! But he can't be Bolognese, must come from around Rome.' After more than a century of unification Italy is still a country of regional differences: the two tiny entities of Emilia and Romagna, for instance, became administratively one in 1859 but, to this day, the Emilians, south of Bologna, like their *ciccioli* dry and crisp (*ciccioli* being pork trimmings rendered of their fat and pressed into sliceable loaves), the Romagnoli, in Bologna and the north, richer and softer.

Every few yards, it seems, in Bologna's twenty-five miles of arcaded streets, there is a window dressed with loaves or pasta in various shapes; sausages or cheeses; cakes and other kickshaws; or everything at once. And the knowledgeable shopkeeper will tell you that the *cottechino*, big, rich boiling sausage, is from Modena, as is *zampone*, which is a pig's trotter stuffed with the same: that the best bread is from Ferrara ('their water is better than ours'), thirty miles away; Parma, which is sixty, with Reggio nell'Emilia, forty, produces the ever-to-be-glorified Parmesan cheese.

'The king of cheeses,' says Antonio Brini in his shop in the Via Ugo Bassi and, with a magnanimous nod in the direction of Milan, 'and Gorgonzola is the queen.' He has been tasting and choosing since he was a lad and guides his customers through his stock of 180 Italian cheeses with unabated enthusiasm.

As we tasted various vintages of his Parmesan we learned that it comes from a legally delimited area around Parma and Reggio, its rind stamped with its *denominazione*, like a wine and, also as with wines, some cheeses will not mature after the required two summers' ageing and will be sold as table cheese, not for cooking. Others mature for longer, the price increasing accordingly: this is the cheese that is grated over your dish as it is put before you in the local restaurants, but it is good on its own, too, broken in chunks from big wedges, strong yet with a mildly sweet, nutty under-taste, and clean at the finish.

The whey from the cheese-making goes to feed fat the pigs from which Parma hams are cut and cured, and the even more delicate *culatello di zibello*, which we have seen nowhere else in Italy. Mouth-waterers such as these can be found at Tamburini, in the Via Caprarie, probably the best-known, best-stocked and busiest of the local grub emporia, with its spit at one end, on which joints of beef and veal and pork, as well as birds, turn over a log fire and, at the back, the nimble-fingered pasta-makers, so that everything in the shop is as fresh as can be.

As a centre for business conventions and such, Bologna is used to foreign visitors—from Britain, there are three Alitalia flights a week (four in summer) from Heathrow to Marconi Airport, 7kms from the city centre, and British Airways flights on alternate days. But Bologna does not set out to woo the tourist—one is hard put to it to find even a picture-postcard kiosk. The restaurants have such splendid material at hand, though, and such knowing customers to please that they must be among the best in Italy. No groups or chains here—every restaurant individually or family owned, like the handsome Tre Frecce in the Strada Maggiore, run by Signor and Signora Ezio and their talented young chef, so self-confident as to have declined a Michelin entry: no *nouvelle cuisine* here. Or small co-operatives, like the similarly handsome Diana, in the Via dell'Indipendenza, owned jointly by manager, chef and accountant, also serving traditional regional food, differing only in style from more bustling bourgeois places such as Cesari in the Via Carbonesi and Da Nello in the Via Montegrappa, where you tuck napkin into neckband and get down to it. Three courses at the noblest of them, or at the particularly pleasing La Filoma in Parma, with a carafe of the house wine, could cost less than £20 a head.

Local wines go with local food. Antonio Brini likes one of the light *frizzante*—semi-sparkling—wines to freshen his palate between cheeses he is tasting, and there is much to be said for the true Lambrusco—not the one sweetened for the American market, which the locals themselves scorn, as 'Lambruscola', but the light, dry red wine, served cool, that foams into the glass and then settles down to a refreshing prickle, justly claimed as the right companion to such rich dishes as *cottechino* and such flavoury cheeses as Parmesan. There are white equivalents, such as the dry Albana and a Malvasia that is as fragrant as an Alsace Gewürztraminer and as flavoury and dry in the mouth. Those who prefer wines that do not fizz do well with the local Sangiovese (from the same grape as Chianti) and the white Trebbiano (like a dry Orvieto).

A whole range can be tasted at the regional wine museum in the drawbridged castle at Dozza, twenty miles from Bologna, where there is a first-class restaurant, Canè, with ten rooms at £20 a night and the Michelin rocking-chair symbol that indicates peace and quiet. Shouldn't mind staying there for a bit, seeing that we came back from the knife-and-fork paradise with digestions unimpaired, not an ounce more on our bones than when we went and—our friends tell us—with self-satisfied smirks on our faces.

NOTE: Prices quoted are as early in 1987, at 2000 lire to the pound. C.R.

from Punch Food and Drink Extra, July 1987

VIVA ITALIA

My God, he's an impudent fella!
—That girl that he showed round the cellar
Lost her *status quo ante*
Between the Chianti
And the magnums of Valpolicella . . .

(Which reminds me of Asti Spumante,
A wine that I'm more *pro* than *anti*—
The only thing is
That this fizz aphrodis-
-iac leads to *delicto flagrante* . . .)

from Lickerish Limericks

NOBODY KNOWS THE TRUFFLES I'VE SEEN

BURTON ANDERSON

IT'S NOT so surprising that truffle is the derivative of trifle in English or that *truffeltruffé* has to do with trickery in French, since users of those languages have been fed trivial portions of *tuber melanosporum* for ages, while being led to believe that those 'black diamonds' were somehow worth the fanfare and the price. Not that there is anything particularly wrong with black truffles, whose elusive fragrance adds a certain something to such culinary extravagances as Paul Bocuse's *soupe aux truffes* and, when cubed, look dandy in aspic and *foie gras*. But as any habitual user of *tuber magnatum* (or, in the more descriptive Italian, *tubero di Afrodite*) could tell you, once you've had white truffles you'll never go back to black.

Since *tartufi bianchi* grow almost exclusively in Italy, they are consumed mainly by Italian gastronomes who tolerate neither trifles nor trickery in their rites of autumn. Though found in special subterranean places up and down the Apennines as far south as Calabria, white truffles have their mecca in the north, at Alba, the Piedmontese city which also happens to be the capital of Barolo and Barbaresco. Not surprisingly, the bouquet of those regal red wines is said to include the odour of truffles, as well as the requisite violets and tar.

Truffles belong to the branch of the fungus family known as *tuberales*, of which there are some 30 species in Europe, the most prized being the white *magnatum* and the black *melanosporum*. Though Italy is a major source of both, most of the black—found mainly around the Umbrian towns of Norcia and Spoleto—are charitably shipped to France to become *truffes du Périgord*. Certain localities in central Italy, most notably Acqualagna in the Marches, boast of the superiority of their own white truffles, though it is hardly a secret that the choicest find their way north to Piedmont to become *tartufi di Alba*. Still, as cognoscenti insist, when conditions of climate are right (relatively damp and chilly), the chalky clay terrain of the Langhe hills around Alba produces what are arguably the most perfumed and indisputably the most expensive of truffles.

Piedmontese hosts generally use a small plane with a razor-sharp blade to shave the raw truffles in flakes over the dish. To avoid expensive misunderstandings they wait for the customer to tell them when to stop. But even if the finest *tartufi di Alba* can cost nearly £1,000 a kilo, the halt order rarely comes before an exquisitely scented layer worth its weight in gold leaf covers the plate.

The colour of truffles is not distinctly black or white but covers a spectrum of relatively dark to light earthy hues. The *melanosporum* come in a dusky brown that could make them mistakable for chocolate truffles. The *magnatum* come in a mottled grey-beige and look something like runty potatoes that have undergone a shotgun attack. The essential difference is in smell. You have to get up close to pick out the odour of the black, but a sharp nose could sniff out a ripe white truffle from across a football pitch, let alone a dining room.

Still, even in this nation of poets and philosophers, the consensus seems to be that the odour of a white truffle is so special that it's indescribable, beyond the elementary *profumo di tartufo*, of course. Those who cite damp earth, herbs, underbrush, soft cheeses, raw vegetables, armpits and various fuels are doing this noblest of funghi an injustice. (Yet the tale of the truffle in the hand baggage on a jumbo jet that had the crew—obviously not Italian—searching for gas leaks from Milan to New York seems to be authentic).

Some human beings are supposedly able to detect the odour of truffles underground, though that feat is usually left to trained mongrels and, rarely nowadays, pigs. Truffles grow next to the new roots of trees, including oak, walnut, poplar, willow, beech and pine. But even if they tend to originate in the same areas, knowing just where to dig for them and when involves considerable experience and intuition. Some *tartufieri* work without dogs, relying on secrets passed down through the generations in their nocturnal treasure hunts. The tricks of the trade begin with making the rounds unobserved, which may require frequent weaves, feints and backtracking, and, of course, means leaving no trace of digging. The rewards can be handsome, but to those who hunt them, truffles, more than a source of income, are a mark of pride and distinction, more than something dug from the earth like potatoes, they are regarded as *objets d'art*. The uncovering of a large, firm, fragrant truffle is the moment of glory that makes those all-night excursions through the damp woods and fields of the Langhe worthwhile. A *tartufiere* would never himself consume such a prize, but he might be as likely to present it to a special friend as sell it.

As any connoisseur can tell you, truffles, like wine, have good years and bad, though a great vintage year for Barolo (invariably hot and dry) may well be a poor one for *tartufi*. In most years, white truffles reach their prime of aroma in mid-November, about two months after the first rains of late summer, but the price usually hits a peak just before Christmas and New Year's Eve when every restaurateur in northwestern Italy wants *tartufi* on the menu.

86

Alba, as well as the neighbouring town of Asti, has a truffle market from October through the holiday season. It becomes most active toward dawn as the *tartufieri* arrive with their night's harvest. Restaurateurs, shopkeepers and other heavy users converge on the trufflers to bargain in dialects that few outsiders, even other Italians, can comprehend, apart from the *lire* figures that are bandied about in the millions. The exchanges between the buyers, who tend to be shrewd, and the hunters, who tend to be stubborn, can go on for hours, though the finest truffles are snapped up quickly no matter what the price. But more about the markets later.

In recent times a brisk export business has developed in white truffles, though it often follows a pattern similar to that of drug smuggling since a carrier can never be certain of how a customs official who has never known its charms might react when confronted with Aphrodite's tuber. Even when packed in jars of rice or wrapped in layers of aluminium foil, that *profumo di tartufo* can pervade a room. Truffles can be tinned or frozen, but only to gratify the desperate. To international traffickers spoilage is as great a risk as discovery, since truffles begin losing their intensity of aroma as soon as they are dug from the earth and unless kept cool and nearly (but not quite) dry can deteriorate or rot in a matter of hours.

I hope I don't sound excessively sentimental in agreeing that white truffles in London, New York or Singapore could never be the same as they are in Alba. For *tartufi* to the normally circumspect Piedmontese are more than a pleasure of the table. They represent a rare touch of the exorbitant, a flight of fancy. Needless to say, they are also considered to be an aphrodisiac. Truffles, more than anything else in Piedmont's autumn bounty, add a welcome note to the coming of another rigid winter.

None of the world's cuisines is so delectably suited to the white truffle as is Piedmont's or, more precisely, Alba's, though the cooking of Asti presents a close rival. Around Alba, white truffles are regularly served with *tajarin* (slender pasta noodles), *carne cruda* or *carpaccio* (paper thin slices of raw veal), *risotto* and *fonduta* (cheese and egg fondue), and occasionally with braised beef and stews, though there are hundreds of other recipes. They are rarely cooked, since heating reduces their aroma and flavour, though one of the favourite recipes elsewhere combines truffles with Parmesan cheese and butter placed under a grill just long enough to start the delectable mass melting. Umbrians often shave their local truffles over *tagliatelli con ragù*, a delicious combination that elicits expressions of horror and disbelief from Piedmontese. So tradition-minded are they that if a local chef dared to cook a fine white truffle (or, worse yet, a bad one) in a soup, he would surely be run out of town.

When I referred to 'normally circumspect Piedmontese' a couple of paragraphs back, I did not have in mind Giacomo Bologna, who is no doubt the region's best-known dealer in truffles. Giacomo also produces wines (including the extraordinary Barbera known as Bricco dell'Uccellone) and raises thoroughbred race horses, activities which might distinguish him as a country gentleman were it not for the Rabelaisian appetite and wit that have earned him nationwide notoriety as a figure several sizes larger than life.

It was with Giacomo one chilly November morn that I first visited the truffle markets of Asti and Alba after a night in his hometown of Rocchetta Tanaro, which despite its outside appearance of a peaceful *paese*, had been depicted by insiders as an 'open loony bin' or 'Disneyland for the deranged'. I soon discovered why.

My first visit began decorously enough one Saturday evening with a heavily truffled dinner accompanied by Barolo and Barbaresco at the Bologna family inn. (It was there that Giacomo, confronted a while back with a customer's complaint about overcooked asparagus tips in his risotto, apologized and nonchalantly sailed the plate out the window. The inn has since closed, not because of Giacomo's antics, which drew customers from all over Europe, but because Mamma Bologna got tired of cooking.) The evening began to liven up as local wines gave way first to Romanée-Conti and then a magnum of the champagne that Moët & Chandon had created for the wedding of Prince Rainier and Grace Kelly. The events that followed, I was assured, were routine during the weekend in Rocchetta Tanaro.

Toward midnight we popped down to the pub to find a gathering of dignitaries—the mayor, the count, a noted artist, the yachtsman who had lost a hefty bet that a concrete craft which took him a year to build would float, among others—applauding the local physician, who was perched on a pool table, strumming a guitar and intoning lusty ditties about his fellow citizens' maladies and quirks. At the end of each tune, wine was ordered along with a couple of dozen glasses, only a few of which could be filled and drunk before the company, pounding fists on the shaky wooden table, had bounced the entire contents to the floor. As the owner cheerfully swept up the pieces, a barmaid would bring a new round and the doctor would shift into his next tune. This version of group therapy Rocchetta style continued for an hour or so until the owner informed us apologetically that he had no more glasses, a signal that it was time to move on to Giacomo's *cantina* to 'tutor' the new wine.

There the mayor, the count and the doctor mounted the massive oak casks and, springing nimbly from one to another, used poles to prod the fermentation caps down into the wine. Meanwhile, the remaining *bons vivants* canvassed Giacomo's reserves for something liquid to ward off the chill. I spotted a bottle of Bruno Giacosa Barbaresco Santo Stefano 1971 (which had been described by a respected critic as the best wine ever made in Italy), but since it was freezing cold, I suggested that we set it aside for lunch. Nothing of the sort, said our host, who insisted that we drink it immediately. A desperate search for an opener came to naught, but Giacomo soon located a hammer and with a deft stroke decapitated the bottle without spilling a drop. After sampling a bit from a tumbler, he agreed it was cool, but no problem, we could warm it on the cellar heater, an immense kerosene-fuelled, turn-of-the-century contraption which he ignited with a match and a resounding roar. While the revered Giacosa Barbaresco was left on top to *chambré*, the artist and yachtsman plied the company with champagne, the only thing in sight that didn't require a hammer to open. Only later, amidst laughter and song, did we remember the Giacosa Barbaresco, but, alas, it had reached the temperature of Paul Bocuse's soup. Not to worry, said Giacomo, who stuffed a wad of paper in the jagged neck and set it aside for lunch. (It turned out to be excellent, though it no longer smelled of truffles either white or black.)

Some of us had hoped to get a little sleep before parting for the truffle markets, but Giacomo wouldn't hear of it as he led us on a raid of the local bakeries so that we'd have something warm in our stomachs before beginning the day's work. The first stop, where we had to force the door, was for pizza fresh from the oven, the second for a species of deep-fried jelly rolls known aptly as *bombe*. Giacomo polished off an even dozen before we set off into the frigid pre-dawn fog for Asti. When I remarked to another outsider that I hadn't been able to pay for anything during the night nor had I noticed any money change hands, he mumbled something about a barter system that you'd have to be as wacky as the natives to comprehend. Anyway, he pointed out, here they reckon that anyone who survives a *Walpurgisnacht* in Rocchetta deserves to go gratis.

The highlight of the market was watching Giacomo, his girth form-fitted into a mammoth macintosh, rapidly making the rounds, stuffing truffles into cloth napkins, pockets and a large plastic sack, while teasing and joking with the *tartufieri*, who seemed as delighted by the exchanges as were members of the boisterous entourage that followed him. Between markets, Giacomo revealed that at Asti he usually picked up his bargains, and at Alba, if truffles were up to standard, his prestige items. But even there the only place I saw money change hands was at a bar in Alba where we stopped for a morning plate of *prosciutto*.

We arrived back in Rocchetta a couple of hours before lunchtime, but the suggestion of sleep was vetoed since friends and clients, mainly restaurateurs, were arriving from Milan, Turin and Genoa and would need to be wined and dined before setting off for home in their truffle-scented autos. As the afternoon degenerated into evening, the last thing I remember before falling asleep on a nearby divan was our host shaving truffles over the back of the hand that I had extended in a vain effort to stop him. If I recall correctly, we were then on the second helping of the third course, a lovely *brasato* cooked in Barolo, and as if I could possibly have doubted it, he assured me with a Rabelaisian leer that it was not to worry: like everything else in Rocchetta Tanaro, these were on the house.

from The Sunday Times Wine Club Magazine

The oddest breakfast I ever heard of was sampled by my father who was staying the night in a country house in Calabria, near Squillace. It consisted of a young cuttlefish, or octopus, in a tumbler, with a glass of brandy.

Sacheverell Sitwell: *Truffle Hunt*, 1953

MEDITERRANEAN FEAST

ALAN JENKINS

At a table in a fisherman's house in Sète
the fisherman's son and ten or twelve of us, his
   friends—
French and English, the Algerian girl—all sat
and opened oysters with our bare hands,

oysters from a barrel that was sprigged with seaweed,
bottomless, as though he had sunk a well
to a salt-water lake below the house, an oyster-bed.
I plunged in for another crusted shell

and it released the reek of seaweed and sea, reek of a
   girl.
The barrel stood as high as our chests
and the plates were stacked with mother-of-pearl.
I watched the black points of Khedidja's breasts

jiggling inside her shirt, and flushed with *apéros*
and *vin rosé*, I wanted to still them, so thought I'd try
to sit her on my lap like a powdered fop from Paris
in *Le déjeuner d'huitres* by Jean François de Troy.

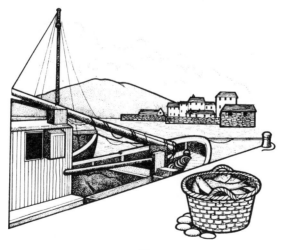

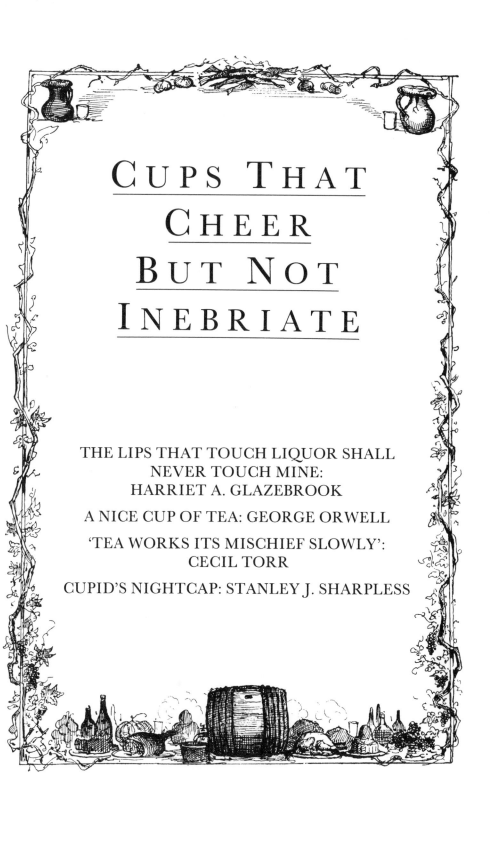

CUPS THAT CHEER BUT NOT INEBRIATE

THE LIPS THAT TOUCH LIQUOR SHALL
NEVER TOUCH MINE:
HARRIET A. GLAZEBROOK

A NICE CUP OF TEA: GEORGE ORWELL

'TEA WORKS ITS MISCHIEF SLOWLY':
CECIL TORR

CUPID'S NIGHTCAP: STANLEY J. SHARPLESS

THE LIPS THAT TOUCH LIQUOR SHALL NEVER TOUCH MINE

HARRIET A. GLAZEBROOK

The *Compleat Imbiber* has always inclined an ear to, and provided a magnanimous platform for, its abstaining fellow-creatures, and if Miss Glazebrook's touching verses are not so powerful as The Great McGonagall's prose piece, *The First Man Who Threw Peas at me Was a Publican*, printed (to great acclaim from its readers) in Imbiber No. 4, 1961, they do at any rate scan . . . C.R.

Alice Lee stood awaiting her lover one night,
Her cheeks flushed and glowing, her eyes full of light.
She had placed a sweet rose 'mid her wild flowing hair;
No flower of the forest e'er looked half so fair
As she did that night, as she stood by the door
Of the cot where she dwelt by the side of the moor.

She heard a quick step coming over the moor,
And a merry voice which she had oft heard before;
And ere she could speak a strong arm held her fast,
And a manly voice whispered, 'I've come, love, at last.
I'm sorry that I've kept you waiting like this,
But I know you'll forgive me, then give me a kiss.'

But she shook the bright curls on her beautiful head,
And she drew herself up while quite proudly she said,
'Now, William, I'll prove if you really are true,
For you say that you love me—I don't think you do;
If really you love me you must give up the wine,
For the lips that touch liquor shall never touch mine.'

He looked quite amazed. 'Why, Alice, 'tis clear
You really are getting quite jealous, my dear.'

94

'In that you are right,' she replied; 'for, you see,
You'll soon love the liquor far better than me.
I'm jealous, I own, of the poisonous wine,
For the lips that touch liquor shall never touch mine.'

He turned, then, quite angry. 'Confound it!' he said,
'What nonsense you've got in your dear little head;
But I'll see if I cannot remove it from hence.'
She said, ''Tis not nonsense, 'tis plain common-sense:
And I mean what I say, and this you will find,
I don't often change when I've made up my mind.'

He stood all irresolute, angry, perplexed:
She never before saw him look half so vexed;
But she said, 'If he talks all his life I won't flinch;'
And he talked, but he never could move her an inch.
He then bitterly cried, with a look and a groan,
'O Alice, your heart is as hard as a stone.'

But though her heart beat in his favour quite loud,
She still firmly kept to the vow she had vowed;
And at last, without even a tear or a sigh,
She said, 'I am going, so, William, goodbye.'
'Nay, stay,' he then said, 'I'll choose one of the two—
I'll give up the liquor in favour of you.'

Now, William had often great cause to rejoice
For the hour he had made sweet Alice his choice;
And he blessed through the whole of a long, useful life,
The fate that had given him his dear little wife.
And she, by her firmness, won to us that night
One who in our cause is an ornament bright.

Oh! that each fair girl in our abstinence band
Would say: 'I'll ne'er give my heart or my hand
Unto one who I ever had reason to think
Would taste one small drop of the vile, cursed drink;'
But say, when you are wooed, 'I'm a foe to the wine,
And the lips that touch liquor shall never touch mine.'

from Michael R. Turner, Parlour Poetry, 1967

A NICE CUP OF TEA

GEORGE ORWELL

IF YOU look up 'tea' in the first cookery book that comes to hand you will probably find that it is unmentioned; or at most you will find a few lines of sketchy instructions which give no ruling on several of the most important points.

This is curious, not only because tea is one of the mainstays of civilisation in this country, as well as in Eire, Australia and New Zealand, but because the best manner of making it is the subject of violent disputes.

When I look through my own recipe for the perfect cup of tea, I find no fewer than eleven outstanding points. On perhaps two of them there would be pretty general agreement, but at least four others are acutely controversial. Here are my own eleven rules, every one of which I regard as golden:

First of all, one should use Indian or Ceylonese tea. China tea has virtues which are not to be despised nowadays—it is economical, and one can drink it without milk—but there is not much stimulation in it. One does not feel wiser, braver or more optimistic after drinking it. Anyone who uses that comforting phrase 'a nice cup of tea' invariably means Indian tea. Secondly, tea should be made in small quantities—that is, in a teapot. Tea out of an urn is always tasteless, while army tea, made in a cauldron, tastes of grease and whitewash. The teapot should be made of china or earthenware. Silver or Britannia-ware pots produce inferior tea and enamel pots are worse: though curiously enough a pewter teapot (a rarity nowadays) is not so bad. Thirdly, the pot should be warmed beforehand. This is better done by placing it on the hob than by the usual method of swilling it out with hot water. Fourthly, the tea should be strong. For a pot holding a quart, if you are going to fill it nearly to the brim, six heaped teaspoons would be about right. In a time of rationing this is not an idea that can be realised on every day of the week, but I maintain that one strong cup of tea is better than 20 weak ones. All true tea-lovers not only like their tea strong, but like it a little stronger with each year that passes—a fact which is recognised in the extra ration issued to old-age pensioners.* Fifthly, the tea should be put straight into the pot. No strainers, muslin bags or other devices to imprison the tea. In some countries teapots are fitted with little dangling baskets under the spout to catch the stray leaves, which are supposed to be harmful. Actually one can swallow tea-leaves in considerable quantities without ill effect, and if the tea is not loose in the pot it never infuses properly. Sixthly, one should take the teapot to the kettle and not the other way about. The water should be actually boiling at the moment of impact, which means that one should keep it on the flame while one pours. Some people add that one should only use water that has been freshly brought to the boil, but I have never noticed that this makes any difference. Seventhly, after making the tea, one should stir it, or better, give the pot a good shake, afterwards allowing the leaves to settle. Eighthly, one should drink out of a breakfast cup—that is the cylin-drical type of cup, not the flat, shallow type. The breakfast cup holds more, and with the other kind one's tea is always half cold before one has well started on it. Ninthly, one should pour the cream off the milk before using it for tea. Milk that is too creamy always gives tea a sickly taste. Tenthly, one should pour tea into the cup first. This is one of the most controversial points of all; indeed in every family in Britain there are probably two schools of thought on the subject. The milk-first school can bring forward some fairly strong arguments, but I maintain that my own argument is unanswerable. This is that, by putting the tea in first and then stirring as one pours, one can exactly regulate the amount of milk whereas one is liable to put in too much milk if one does it the other way round.

Lastly, tea—unless one is drinking it in the Russian style—should be drunk *without sugar*. I know very well that I am in a minority here. But still, how can you call yourself a true tea-lover if you destroy the flavour of your tea by putting sugar in it? It would be equally reasonable to put pepper or salt. Tea is meant to be bitter, just as beer is meant to be bitter. If you sweeten it, you are no longer tasting the tea, you are merely tasting the sugar; you could make a very similar drink by dissolving sugar in plain hot water.

Some people would answer that they don't like tea in itself, that they only drink it in order to be warmed and stimulated, and they need sugar to take

---

* Wartime rationing was still in force in 1946. C.R.

the taste away. To those misguided people I would say: Try drinking tea without sugar for, say, a fortnight and it is very unlikely that you will ever want to ruin your tea by sweetening it again.

These are not the only controversial points that arise in connection with tea-drinking, but they are sufficient to show how subtilised the whole business has become. There is also the mysterious social etiquette surrounding the teapot (why is it considered vulgar to drink out of your saucer, for instance?) and much might be written about the subsidiary uses of tea-leaves, such as telling fortunes, predicting the arrival of visitors, feeding rabbits, healing burns and sweeping the carpet. It is worth paying attention to such details as warming the pot and using water that is really boiling, so as to make quite sure of wringing out of one's ration the twenty good, strong cups that two ounces, properly handled, ought to represent.

from Evening Standard, 12 January 1946

'TEA WORKS ITS MISCHIEF SLOWLY'

CECIL TORR

On the whole, less harm is done by cider than by tea; but cider gets more blame, as its ill effects are visible at once, whereas tea works its mischief slowly. Nobody says anything against tea-drinking now; but Parson Davy in his *System of Divinity*, vol. xix, page 235, which he printed at Lustleigh in 1803, spoke with indignation of 'the immeasurable use of that too fashionable and pernicious plant, which weakens the stomach, unbraces the nerves, and drains the very vitals of our national wealth; to which nevertheless our children are as early and as carefully enured, from the very breast, as if the daily use of it were an indispensable duty which they owed to God and their country.' And in his *Letter to a Friend concerning Tea*, published in 1748, John Wesley spoke of tea-drinking as tea-drinkers speak of drinking alcohol now: 'wasteful, unhealthy self-indulgence'—'no other than a slow poison'—'abhor it as a deadly poison, and renounce it from this very hour.'

Cecil Torr (b. 1857), *Small Talk at Wreyland*, First Series, 1918

99

A CUPID'S
NIGHTCAP

STANLEY J. SHARPLESS

*Lines written upon hearing the startling news
that cocoa is, in fact, a mild aphrodisiac*

Half past nine—high time for supper;
'Cocoa, love?' 'Of course, my dear.'
Helen thinks it quite delicious,
John prefers it now to beer.
Knocking back the sepia potion,
Hubby winks, says, 'Who's for bed?'
'Shan't be long,' says Helen softly,
Cheeks a faintly flushing red.
For they've stumbled on the secret
Of a love that never wanes,
Rapt beneath the tumbled bedclothes,
Cocoa coursing through their veins.

TALES TO TELL

MONSIEUR DODIN-
BOUFFANT MAKES
AN END OF IT:
A STORY

MARCEL ROUFF

THE Prince's Dinner' as they called it in the town once its details became known, was one of the triumphs of Dodin-Bouffant's career. Of course his four disciples did not hold their tongues for long: that very evening the Café de Saxe knew that the day had been a glorious one for the city—three days later the entire province shared their civic pride and the event was discussed in many inns, from the taverns of Geneva to the famous 'Golden Pike' at Lyon. The hero of the day took no pride in it other than that of having produced a masterpiece *ad majorem gastronomiae gloriam* and written a fine page in the history of the table. In his equitable soul, Dodin rendered to his cook the homage which was her due and loyally attributed to her a fair share of their success. The conceit, its direction, to a great extent the actual substance of the marvellous meal were his own work, but Adèle Pidou, he admitted to himself, had been the incomparable handmaiden of his brain.

Adèle Pidou! The charm and the torment of the great man's existence! His main reason for living and his rack! It will be remembered that the death of Eugénie Chatagne was followed for Dodin, thenceforth deprived of that great artist, by a procession of aspirants to her awesome functions. During gloomy days, Dodin surveyed a series of faces devoid of any spark of genius, of any great passion, lifeless eyes adapted far more to following the flight of iridescent gadflies over muddy cow-flanks than to the contemplation of that moist gold which, little by little, colours the skin of fine fat birds, stuffed with butter and patiently basted. But suddenly, just as the desperate *gastronome* was seriously contemplating doffing the old magistrate's frock coat and replacing it by the white attire of a cook to ensure his own comfortable living and the delight of his friends, Adèle Pidou, last in the line, appeared upon his doorstep. Short, stocky, her round and jovial head lit up by canny eyes, haloed in a very clean but very worn calico kerchief, she placed upon the master's desk without ceremony her basket in which a squawking duck kicked at the fresh vegetables with its tied legs. Then, quite unembarrassed, she settled down in a comfortable armchair. Oh! Dodin had no need, to save them from the wanderings of temptation, to put his hands in his pockets. The fat thighs, overfull bodice, double chin and somewhat faded hair of his visitor imbued him with invincible respect. After a long conversation in which her ingenuous and unconscious but very sure taste soon became apparent to the psychologist, he took her, according to his customary ritual, but with marked consideration, to visit the dining-room and the kitchen. The cordon bleu's eyes, with an odd gleam of interest and evident enthusiam, pleasurably caressed all the complicated and ingenious appointments. Dodin followed her gaze and dissected it with emotion. Indeed, just as a thoroughbred horse leaps forward into space, or as a writer quivers with impatience before a blank sheet of paper and a well-trimmed pen, so Adèle Pidou could not restrain herself; she began, for no reason at all save the pleasure of touching them, to seize the handles of frying-pans and skillets, of copper saucepans, to stroke the rounded flanks of the earthenware pots, to feel the bottles of spices, the boxes of ingredients, to open them, sniff them, examine the stove, inspect the spits and the fish-kettles. Dodin, throbbing with hope, allowed her to please herself. Perhaps, at last . . . And, seated upon the chairs of the Temple they resumed a conversation already more intimate, more confiding.

'Yes,' said Adèle Pidou suddenly, 'don't know, but p'raps what I cooked up t'other day for our little Louis' christening might've pleased your Honour. There's my young brother, Jean-Marie, who'd poached a lovely 'hairy'—a young hare, you know, but big already—what they call a Capuchin. Well, for a change, and to give 'em a treat, I thought of soaking it in our own *marc*, that we distil ourselves, 'n then to bone it gently when it'd taken properly, and to stuff its belly and stomach with a sort of stuffing I'd mixed with his own liver and some pig, and bread-crumbs and a kind of truffle we find near our barn by an oak, and then a little of the preserved turkey we make for the winter. And I cooked the whole beastie, with his bulging belly sewn up, in a sauce full of good red wine and good cream. Should have seen the helpings afterwards! 'Twasn't bad. Might've pleased Your Honour. It put a well-being in the whole banquet!'

Needless to say that Adèle Pidou was immediately taken on to the staff of Dodin-Bouffant on terms which she fixed herself, and that, thanks to the magistrate's deplorable weakness, she became the mistress of the house without striking a blow. Dodin, from then on, lived, according to the season, in an uninterrupted dream of veal-birds with scented stuffings, unbelievable legs of mutton under the raised skin of which lurked prodigious forcemeat balls, fricassees which made him want to live for ever, sheeps' tongues 'in curl papers' (*en papillotes*), Gascon beef-skirts, Fonbonne soups, fish broths, ducks *à la Nivernaise*, 'grenadins' of chicken, jugged goose-livers, game sausages, stewed cockscombs, chickens *à la Favorite*, shoulders of lamb *à la Dauphine*.

From savoury sausages of sucking-pig trotters in milk he went on to patties of perch and baby-quail tarts; from pâtés of plover fillets to trout in Chartreuse. No sooner was the period of baby rabbits *à la Zephyr* and baby chicks *à la follette* over, than he saw appear upon his blessed table truffles *à la Maréchale*, shrimps on the spit, partridges in their own juice, 'minute' quails, larks *au gratin*, moulds of pheasant, Polish hare, thrushes *à la Gendarme*; and later jellied boar, snipe *à la poulette*, and sandpipers *au Pontife*. Not to mention eggs *à la mouillette*, *à la bonne amie*, or *à la vestale*, omelets with anchovies *à la servante*, or *au joli coeur*, nor roe tarts, nor eels *à la Choisi*, pike *à la Mariée*, carp in Frock Coats, artichokes in Champagne wine, cardoons St Cloud, noodles with bacon, steamed mushrooms, 'tobacco-pouch' spinach, nor desserts, marchpanes, compotes, waffles and biscuits.

In this abundance of delights, surrounded by the charm of these touching meals of which each one was a new joy and none of which, unless he requested it be prepared in the same way, included a dish which had already figured upon his table, Dodin lived days of sweet satisfaction. His life, disrupted by the death of his faithful assistant, had gloriously regained its balance; from beyond the grave Eugénie Chatagne had handed Adèle Pidou the torch of the great tradition. Perhaps, and Dodin often thought about these mysteries of fate, perhaps it was her free spirit which had led to the august and triumphal kitchen where she had officiated for so long, the woman worthy to succeed her. Having succeeded in reaching the peaks of human perfection in his art, having obtained for himself the unvarying marvels of his 'daily bread', the old magistrate, ever preaching the work of taste, suspected that his twilight would be the radiant conclusion of a beautiful life. From then on he awaited death, which he did not desire but did not fear, in that joyous and peaceful repletion which so many tormented and incomplete artists have never known; sure of ending his long and laborious career in the fulfilment of fruitful effort, of complete achievement, and in the ever-renewed enjoyment of each meal. Dodin finally knew all the moral and material satisfactions which cookery will yield in return for the honours due to it.

And yet, a terrible storm threatened his happiness; so true is it that our earthly condition is essentially unstable, that no man may be proclaimed happy before his death, so it is also true that the pride of princes often leads them to scorn the elementary laws of human morality and decent shame! The Prince of Eurasia dared to envy Dodin-Bouffant, his host, and coveted Adèle Pidou, the fine craftswoman of the meal which he now saw in an entirely new light. At first, his private secretary was seen roaming the market, asking questions. The next day, he took a hired cabriolet, left the city gates, and then, abandoning the vehicle in front of the salt stores, stepped with some hesitation towards the Parcels Office where Adèle went almost daily to collect some delivery of victuals. Another day, again, he was seen patiently mounting guard before the shop where Foujoullaz sold delicate early vegetables; at last, he was seen after nightfall in a suspicious waiting attitude outside the Tax Collector's gate—a house in which Adèle, her day's work done, was not too proud to visit the old cook in the quiet hours of the evening. These mysterious advances continued for some time before Dodin knew more about them than vague, imprecise rumours, subtle, uncertain noises, whispers without any consistency. This did not prevent his being most anxious about them. As an old magistrate, accustomed to sounding the depths of human hearts, to assembling circumstances in order to discover their real meaning, he half-saw, without daring to reach it, the fatal conclusion that could be drawn from the obstinate presence of the Prince's henchman in places where he was certain to meet Adèle. He had been brought up in a century, moreover, which left in the hearts of the best of Frenchmen only the frailest illusions about the gratitude of the world's Great. Dodin began to fear that he had triumphed too completely over the Heir to Eurasia. He did not quite dare confide his anxiety to Adèle, nor tell her of his fears. She was, as all true artists are, of a varying and awkward disposition, of doubtful and touchy humour, and easily irritated. He feared the possibility of a violent scene with her and a scandal which might, under the impetus of irresistible rage, deprive him of her genius. And then, was there not also at the very back of his mind a remnant of pride which forbade him to show too clearly how indispensable she had become to his existence? Could he let her know that she was the absolute sovereign of his life?

Dodin therefore carried around an anxious and tormented soul. Sometimes his imagination invented some eventuality which reason, alas, when it resumed possession of his brain, did not prove to him to be impossible. And this doubt condensed within himself, kept secret, and which he dared confide to no one, so afraid was he of formulating it in precise words, devoured him and sometimes sank him into a truly painful condition of over-excitement.

He would go out panting, bent with sorrow, mopping his brow, to flee— to go and drown his anguish in the infamous vermouths of the Café de Saxe. Noon struck. He would return, head low and despair in his heart. He would sit down and suddenly the blankness of the table-cloth would be illuminated by fillets of farm chicken à la Pompadour, or a mushroom stew in Chambertin, or quail à la Mayence, or pigeons à la Martine which dispersed his sorrow in a moment, as the soft breeze of a summer night scatters the last bitter smoke of burning weeds in the meadows. And the spiritual love he had conceived for the unconscious genius of the woman would seep into him, overwhelm and disarm him. He would apologize to her mentally for having doubted her; he even managed, as he consumed her absolute and perfect cooking, devoid of all weakness, free of any fault, to adorn her massive body with touching illusions, her vulgar face with beauty, and to throw her furtive glances of tenderness.

Dodin-Bouffant was too familiar with the human soul and too sceptical regarding its virtues even to dream of storming at the methods of the Highness who, having been received at his table, could consider thieving from him the happiness of his old age. This ingratitude was but a princely game. Only now and again did he take himself to task for his foolishness in setting ajar the door of his sanctuary for the royal visitor: all his thoughts and all his sufferings were really concentrated upon Adèle's possible departure—Adèle, conquered by golden promises, won over by the solicitations of her vanity; a notice which he awaited with the shudder of the 'little death' between his shoulder blades every time Adèle opened the door, every time he went home, every time he opened his eyes to those calm and pure Jurassic dawns whose tender rosiness accompanied his grilled bacon or his egg *salmis*. His life, under the shadow of this perpetual threat, became a torture that the most skilful inquisitor could not have invented, a torture complicated by his joint desire and fear to speak to the great artist from whose hands he accepted so much suffering and so much joy. This hesitation, to which every hour brought him a contradictory solution, sometimes ended by a furtive trip into town whence he would bring back some soft, silken material, some precious umbrella or chiselled brooch, humble presents which he knew quite well could never compete with the princely fortunes which could not fail to be offered to Adèle Pidou on the day when the secretary finally launched his offensive.

Had he not already launched it? Adèle, there was no possible doubt about it, was preoccupied, nowadays, sometimes dreamy. It even seemed that her natural simplicity was taking on a tinge of unaccustomed pride. She seemed to be turning over in her round head a grave problem which Dodin guessed to be the enigma of her future which she sought to solve. Her eyes often strayed far over the walls of her kitchen, and the unhappy epicure, following their direction, could see in the distance the flamboyant splendours of a palace.

He took good care, out of regard for his dignity, to mention none of his awful bitterness to his companions. But they had no trouble in detecting upon his tired and ageing features the ravages of his distress. They dared not question him, but having dimly guessed that his cook was not uninvolved in the trouble, they feared a catastrophe which lay in wait for them too.

Dodin was warned by the owner of the Café de Saxe that his apprehensions were only too well-founded. It was a terrible piece of news, for, hoping against hope, he still wished to think of his fears as chimerical. At sunset, the innkeeper had seen the cordon bleu crossing the square at the side of the elegant secretary who was speaking feverishly. She did not answer, but nodded her head. Dodin received the blow with dignity and paid for his almond-essence and kirsch, impatient to be alone. He pulled himself together with a great effort feeling, to his surprise, almost relief at no longer struggling with uncertainty. He took an immediate decision. Rather than wait for his life to be shattered, he resolved to make the horrible sacrifice himself. Since his purse was too modest to vie with that of one of the richest princes in Europe, since Adèle had sacrificed, or was about to sacrifice, glory to vainglory and art to gold, he would himself, without awaiting her good pleasure, give her notice. In this way he would embark with dignity and of his own free will upon the obscure renunciation of his work and of his passion until Death should end it all. He pushed the door open resolutely.

Alas, prickly and frowning, for the knowledge of the crime she was about to commit soured her extremely, Adèle successively deposited before her victim roe fritters such as the Gods alone may enjoy and a calf's head in aspic *à la Vieux Lyon* which cast the master's palate, so extremely sensitive and practised, into a profound state of rapture. He threw the faithless one a loving glance and felt that he was properly lost. For, from the bottom of his heart, there rose impetuously a sentiment in which mingled, in fearsome chaos, admiration, gratitude, and, for so many indescribable joys, love. The inconstant creature would leave behind her only disaster and ruin, an empty house, a passion in ashes, a wounded heart. What a vision of oblivion passed before the eyes of that pathetic man! To be alone under this deserted roof! And, to fill the interminable hours of abandonment, to have only the disastrous prospect of vulgar and unappetizing messes! The unfortunate Dodin, urged on by who knows what, probably in the unconscious hope of seducing the woman who already had one foot on the deck of the vessel which was to bear her off for ever, began to pay her a timid and touching court which was, however, greeted with hauteur. Quite incapable himself of renouncing the heavens to which three times daily she opened the portals, he was seized with tremors of apprehension at the horrible idea that the day was nigh when her decision would be peremptorily put before him, and he had no other anxiety, day by day, than that of delaying the evil moment. Adèle, who was in all honesty of a strait-laced disposition and perhaps somewhat surprised to see her virtue attacked at this late date, sometimes deigned an absent-minded response to a fervour devoid of all salaciousness, but quickly resumed her enigmatic air, too evident a proof of her lack of con-viction.

The crisis was imminent. All the premonitory signals announced it. It exploded on the first evening of winter. Dodin, like a sick man who knows himself to be condemned, was devouring in almost ferocious haste what might well be the last delights Adèle Pidou would bestow upon him. He had invited Beaubois, Trifouille, Rabaz and Magot to a dinner which he alone among them knew to be the last.

That night Adèle, after a soup of Spanish cardoon sippets, had presented a superb stuffed eel, surrounded by crystal. It had occurred to her to mix the meat of this creature, pounding it in a mortar, adding cream, breadcrumbs, chives and mushrooms, with truffles. She had wrapped this concoction around the spine of the fish, reconstituting its original shape, and covering it copiously with egg and breadcrumbs, had served it after giving it a fine colour in the oven.

Everyone had already been dazzled. The guests had then seriously tackled the hot *pâté à la Royale*, exclaiming devoutly as they seized a large piece of mutton or a fillet of partridge, or a mouthful of beef which they scooped up with generous gestures from a woodcock gravy and a rich bacon garnish which had absorbed into its thick fat the divine aroma of a clove of garlic.

Adèle, reluctant to give her master the sad news in the emotional atmosphere of a tête-à-tête, in which she would have been alone to confront a despair which she foresaw; considering moreover that the other four gourmets, as priests of the great art and habitual disciples of the Teacher, were entitled to be informed at the same time as Dodin himself; relying also somewhat upon the presence of his friends to cushion a blow she knew would be heavy; Adèle, then, had decided to announce her departure during this meal. She began just as she had laid upon the table a leg of young boar in pastry whose meat she had cushioned against the dough with a delicate hash of duck-livers marinated in champagne liqueur.

She was obviously embarrassed.

'I have to tell these gentlemen . . .'

She did not know what to do with her hands.

'That Monsieur His Highness the Prince . . .'

At the first words Dodin, white, taut, frozen, understood.

'He'd like to take me on . . . because he says, says he, that none of his cooks . . . well, because he was very pleased with the luncheon . . .'

Dodin managed to sketch a bitter smile.

'I didn't want to leave M. Dodin-Bouffant . . . because . . . because it's an honour to serve a master like him . . . such a connoisseur . . . so refined . . . and so good too . . . I must tell Monsieur . . . And then, I know all right that I've learned a lot from Monsieur . . . he's taught me a lot . . . so it's ungrateful . . .'

Beaubois, Rabaz and Magot, Trifouille, understood in turn and their faces, so recently expansive with contentment, suddenly took on that air of painful disappointment characteristic of children trying in vain to contain their tears.

Adèle, who must have spent much time meditating her awkward speech, continued:

'But there it is . . . I'm not as young as I used to be . . . got to think of my old age . . . And when Monsieur has gone, what will become of me?'

This allusion to his death moved neither Dodin nor his friends in the least.

'And I'm not rich, you know . . . So my family advised me . . . to accept the awfully big salary I'm being offered . . . His Excellency the Prince . . .

Imagine ... sixty *écus* every month ... and of course an interest on the cook's perks ... could retire to our farm and be pretty well off ...'

Impelled by a sudden resolution, Dodin rose abruptly, so unexpectedly that Adèle, terrified, thought he was going to strike her, and his friends believed him to be in the grip of violent madness. Very pale, very calm, on the contrary, he took the cook by the hand and very quietly said to her:

'Adèle, I wish to speak to you.'

They both disappeared into the kitchen. A heavy silence descended upon the table, a silence which Magot disturbed only to observe after a few minutes of anguished thought, that the situation would be in no way improved by the loss of the venison if allowed to grow cold. And they began to eat sadly, occasionally allowing to fall from their lips some emotional words about Dodin's misfortune and their own. Then, each in turn, they went back to the dish.

A long half-hour elapsed to the monotonous accompaniment of anxious chewing. At last the kitchen door opened, not without a certain majestic slowness. Dodin, now red in the face, his gaze aflame with a strange triumph and upon his features a sovereign relief, appeared holding a tearful Adèle Pidou by the hand, and spoke these simple words:

'Gentlemen: Madame Dodin-Bouffant.'

from The Passionate Epicure English translation by Claude, London, 1961

Note: The author, Marcel Rouff, was a contemporary of Maurice Saillant ('Prince Élu des Gastronomes') and his co-author in *La France Gastronomique*.

In his introduction to the English edition, Lawrence Durrell suggests that the portrait of Dodin-Bouffant, Falstaffian hero of this mock-heroic novel, owes something to Brillat-Savarin (1755–1826), author of *La Physiologie du Gout*, observing that he, too, came of heroic stock ... Brillat's great-aunt, for instance, died at the age of 93 while sipping a glass of old Virieu, while Pierrette, his sister, uttered (at table) the following last words: '*Vite, apportez-moi le dessert—je sens que je vais passer!*'

C.R.

THE BRESSE
CHICKEN:
A STORY

ANTHELME BRILLAT-SAVARIN

O N O N E of the first days of January this present year, 1825, a young married couple, Monsieur and Madame de Versy by name, were guests at an oyster breakfast.

Such meals are charming, not only because they are composed of tempting dishes, but also because of the gaiety which usually distinguishes them; however, they have the disadvantage of upsetting the rest of the day's arrangements. This was the case on the present occasion. When dinnertime arrived, the pair sat down at table; but it was a mere formality. Madame took a little soup, Monsieur drank a glass of wine and water; some friends dropped in, a game of whist was played, the evening drew to a close, and the couple retired to their bed.

About two o'clock in the morning, Monsieur de Versy awoke, feeling restless; he yawned, and tossed and turned so much that his wife grew alarmed, and asked if he was unwell. 'No, my dear, but I appear to be hungry; I was thinking of that beautiful white Bresse chicken which we were offered for dinner and to which we gave such a cold reception.' 'My dear, to tell the truth, I am as hungry as you are, and now that you have thought of that chicken it must be sent for and eaten.' 'What an idea! The whole house is asleep, and tomorrow everybody will laugh at us.' 'If the whole house is asleep, the whole house must wake up, and we shall not be laughed at for the simple reason that no one will know about it. Besides, who knows if between now and tomorrow one of us may not starve to death? I don't intend running that risk. I'm going to ring for Justine.'

No sooner said than done; and the poor girl, who had supped well and was sleeping as only those can sleep who are nineteen years old and untroubled by dreams of love, was duly awakened.

She arrived all untidy and bleary-eyed, and sat down yawning and stretching her arms.

But this had been an easy task; it still remained to rouse the cook, and that was no small matter; she grumbled, neighed, growled, roared, and snorted. In the end, however, she got out of bed and set her vast circumference in motion.

In the meantime Madame de Versy had put on a dressing-jacket, her husband had made himself presentable, while Justine had spread a cloth on the bed, and brought in the indispensable accessories to an improvised feast.

When everything was ready, the chicken appeared, to be torn apart on the spot and remorselessly devoured.

After this first exploit, husband and wife shared a large Saint-Germain pear, and ate some orange marmalade.

In the intervals they drained a bottle of Graves to the dregs, and declared several times, with variations, that they had never had a more delightful meal.

However, this meal came to an end, as all things must in this world. Justine cleared away the incriminating evidence, and went back to bed; and the conjugal curtain fell upon the participants in the feast.

Next morning, Madame de Versy hurried round to see her friend Madame de Franval, and recounted all that had happened in the night; and it is to that lady's indiscretion that the public owes the present revelation.

She never fails to add that when Madame de Versy came to the end of her story, she coughed twice and blushed furiously.

from La Physologie du Gôut, 1826

APPLEJOHN

FRANK PARRISH

EDGAR'S FARM, near the Wessex village of Medwell Fratra-trorum, included a walled orchard of elderly apple-trees, gnarled like arthritic fingers. The apples were russets, commercially useless, tons of them. They were no good for cider, and they did not keep; but they made good juice. The farmer's wife, anxious to diversify, had ideas about juice. She found a cider-press, scrubbed and repaired it, and put it in the barn. It looked very quaint and was shown to visitors. Friends of the children turned the windlass, and juice oozed into an enamel basin. It was bottled and sold at fêtes. The apple mountain was replaced by a mountain of squashed pips and cores and peel, a vegetable industrial tip, an organic slag-heap. In the spring, pale grass seeded itself on the top.

Against this background—the Alp of apple-cores—began the deplorable episode of Dan Mallett's illicit still.

Dan was young, though of uncertain age; small, though of apparently varying height. He had a wedge-shaped, deeply tanned face, unruly mouse-coloured hair, and blue eyes that got him into and out of trouble. In the course of a week he adopted so many personalities that he became confused about the way he actually thought and talked. He was perhaps most truly himself at five in the morning on the edge of a pheasant preserve. Then he was pretending only to the pheasants, and pretending only that he wasn't there.

Dan knew about Edgar's Farm Apple Juice ('The Juice, the Whole Juice, Nothing but the Juice') because he was a neighbour. He lived with his mother the other side of Medwell, in an eccentric cottage under the tattered fringe of the Priory Woods. Old Mrs Mallett disapproved of her only child with a bitterness she reserved otherwise for greenfly. He was a thriftless runagate, forever wenching, boozing or stealing, when he could by now have been Assistant Manager of the bank in Milchester. Mrs Mallett felt betrayed, and she spread her feelings around her like a fog. It was worse for them both that she was crippled and often in pain.

From the shadow of the apple-cores, and other shadows, Dan emerged on an April day into the Buttermarket in Milchester. People came from the villages to buy things in Milchester; Dan came to sell things. On that visit he had not yet done so. The teaspoons were in his pocket. Down the pavement came a policeman, well known to Dan, a detective-sergeant with a face like a Hereford bullock.

Dan might have been seen to flicker and disappear. He was not sure if he had done so soon enough. He rematerialised in Bellman's Yard, at the end of an alleyway. He slid through the door of a second-hand bookshop. He swam through the booky dust of cavern after cavern, successively darker, and up a ladder to a shelf of 18th-century sermons. He put the teaspoons behind the sermons, descended two shelves, and buried his nose in a leather-bound volume with an incomplete binding. He could only just see to read.

The sergeant steamed in. He spotted Dan half-way up the ladder in the semi-darkness, but he could not make an arrest on any grounds except hatred.

Dan waited on the ladder for the sergeant to stop boiling. While he waited he looked at the book. It had lost its title-page and introduction. It got immediately down to the meat. The book seemed very old but the paper was good and the type legible.

The diligent Husbandman may augment his *Income* while brightening the Hours of his *Leisure* by putting to Profitable Use many Matters which the Improvident will cast aside as Waste. The *Alexandrians* of Antiquity, the prudent *Arabians*, the Medieval *Philosophers* and *Alchemists* were alike vers'd in the delicate Arts of *Distillation*, by the Seeming Magicke of the which your shreds of *Swedish Turnips*, the very Peelings of your *Potatoes*, may be conjur'd into Liquors of exceeding Power and Fragrance.

The text was interrupted by a wood-engraving of what its caption said was a *Pot-Still*. Tiny italic letters freckled the picture, to which there was a key: still, condenser, receiver, water, steam. The fire below the still was identified as fire. It looked pretty simple. The Irish did it, the hill-billies of Tennessee, the crofters of the West Highlands, as well as learned Arabs and alchemists. Surely he, Dan Mallett, once a scholar at the Grammar School, could light a camp-fire under a bucket and catch a bit of steam?

Dan was invited, by an old man in a beret, to pay two pounds for the book. He complained that the loss of binding and title page reduced its value. He got it for a quid. By this time the sergeant had gone away.

Dan was filled with so wild a surmise that he went to the Milchester Public Library, the first time he had done so since his days at the Grammar School. It was full of strip-lighting and people who had a right to be there. Dan slipped shyly into this studious atmosphere, and found the reference section. He perched at a table, with some volumes of an encyclopaedia. He was lately unaccustomed to book study, but he had once been thought good at it. With words and pictures the articles filled out his knowledge.

A girl called Mary Cousins was assistant librarian on duty. She was paid to notice everything that went on. Dan had not noticed her on account of his preoccupation. He was engaged in self-improvement, even to the exclusion of pretty young assistant librarians.

Mary Cousins knew that she had never seen this demure little stranger before, because if she had she would have remembered. It was not that her memory was remarkable but that his eyes were remarkable—a wide and guileless blue, blue for danger, too innocent to be believed. The man was otherwise unremarkable, in face, physique, clothes or manner, but still not quite like anybody else Mary Cousins had ever seen. She had the sense of being about to embark on absurd adventures. She wanted a few of those. She was a girl of more spirit than the job gave her scope for.

She had just broken with her accountant boy friend because he was boring. It was no moment for a nice girl to see Dan Mallett's eyes for the first time.

Dan made notes and copied illustrations. Alcohol boils at 78.3 Centigrade. An accurate thermometer is required, its bulb just below the point at which the steam leaves the still on its way to the condenser. Where could he find a thermometer calibrated right up to boiling-point? The front of a vintage car? The chemistry laboratory at the Technical College?

Between the still and the condenser there were one or two vessels into which less volatile elements dropped out of the steam, to be returned to the still to be boiled up some more. Jars with pipes coming out of the bottom. Were there such jars outside a hospital? Would the Milchester Hospital let him have an old one? The condenser was a spiral pipe in a jacket. Dan began to picture an acre of glassware in the Priory Woods, under some kind of awning to stop the rain putting out his fire.

Ethyl alcohol was what you got in the receiver. But very important were the congeners or congenerics. They were all kinds of other things, in tiny quantities, which went along in the steam and gave you the flavour. Congenerics made plum brandy different from apricot brandy, and Dan's different from any other in the world.

For full strength you did the whole thing twice. Then you could add water if you wanted to. Dan thought he would not.

*   *   *

Mary Cousins, with time on her hands, found herself wondering who the small brown man was, what he normally did, what he was so deeply studying. When he got up to go out for a minute, she strolled over to his table to glance at his books and notes. They could not have been secret, or he would not have left them for anybody to see.

One volume of the encyclopaedia was open at an article entitled *Stills*, with illustrations of scientific and industrial equipment. Oh. The other was open at an article called *Brandy*. There were lists of all the different sorts of brandy, where they came from, how they were distilled. Ah.

The brown man was suddenly there, startling Mary so much that she bit her tongue. She felt herself blushing, caught snooping at his studies.

Dan saw a very pretty girl, unknown to him, looking at his books and probably guessing his secret. He smiled. It was his reassuring smile, with a touch of bashfulness and no more than a hint of lust.

The girl smiled back, blushing for no reason that Dan could see. She turned and went back to her desk by the exit. It was a pleasure to watch her in movement.

She reached the desk and sat down. She was a girl who was graceful at sitting down at a desk. She glanced at Dan. He grinned again, and saluted with his ball-point. Her smile came and went and she became busy with a computer print-out.

Dan turned back to *Brandy*.

Mature in oak casks. Sherry casks best. Where from? Brewer? Wine merchant? Pub going out of business?

Dan was pleased to note that an important improvement to the apparatus was patented in Britain by Aeneas Coffey in 1831. Too late for the diligent Husbandman but in good time for the Priory Wood . . . The Priory Wood— what? Priory Wood Applejack? Too informal, demeaning. We are aiming higher than that. Apple Brandy? Pretentious. Compromise needed.

Applejohn.

With the coining of his brand-name, Dan felt that the back of the job was broken.

He was quite wrong.

Assembling the parts of even the simplest pot-still called for things not used for any other purpose at all.

Dan was employed by the more credulous gentry as a handyman, but he had no metal-working or glass-blowing experience. He could saw a plank or drive in a nail, if he was given plenty of time, but he could not devise vessels with pipes coming into the top and out of the bottom. He did not understand how the diligent Husbandman had come by them. But Dan could be diligent, too, when he was working for himself, and during the summer he gradually collected things with scarcely credible shapes. Among his sources were dumps of wrecked cars, restaurant kitchens to which in the winter he sold pheasants, a builder's merchant visited quietly out of business hours, a wholesale pharmaceutical supplier, on the industrial estate near Milchester station, where he had to pay cash . . .

He secured at a local auction an oak sherry-cask that had held Amontillado and one that had held Oloroso. Applejohn would come sweet and dry. It was weary work with too much bicycling, but a vision of palest gold glimmered on his horizon.

His mother knew he was up to mischief.

He continued to be guided by the diligent Husbandman, but in assembling his apparatus he found that he had to go back to the encyclopaedia. He became a familiar face in the library, and the pretty girl's face became familiar to him.

'What kind of brandy are you going to make?'

Dan, on the steps of the library, was so startled that he dropped a sheaf of notes. They fluttered about the municipal car-park in the fitful July wind.

'Oh, I'm so sorry,' said the pretty librarian, who had grown prettier over the weeks of Dan's occasional visits.

Together they chased Dan's notes, making grabs under the wheels of cars. This ridiculous activity, while driving them apart, brought them close. Mary had come off duty, and was thus able to have a cup of coffee with Dan in 'Pamela's Pantry', beside the betting-shop.

'Applejohn,' said Dan, answering at last her question.

He knew with certainty that, though a public servant, she was not going to rush to the Customs and Excise to lay information about cunning little men with stills in the Priory Woods. Her cheeks were pink from running about in the car-park in the sun.

Her father was a teacher; her mother worked part-time as a doctor's receptionist; they lived on the edge of a town thirty miles away. She herself had A-levels and a Diploma and a desire to do quite different things from any she had ever done.

'I've never drunk Applejack,' she said.

'Nobody's ever drunk Applejohn,' Dan said. 'If they survive, they'll tell their grandchildren about it.'

'May I come and see?'

'You're a kind of fairy godmother to the whole project.'

*　　*　　*

She tried not to look aghast, contemplating the crazy array among the rabbit-holes.

'It's a mite Heath Robinson,' said Dan apologetically. 'Improvisation.'

'*Don't use no green or rotten wood,*' sang Mary to Joan Baez's tune, '*or they'll get you by the smoke.*'

Dan laughed, and kissed her for the first time.

Thereafter it was a game they played together, like good children but not very like, fitting tubes into retorts and stacking wood and redesigning the layout, interrupting with moments of abandon the serious business of the woods.

Dan borrowed a sackful of bricks, and built a kind of barbecue to heat the still. He borrowed some polythene sheeting to keep the rain off his firewood. The place began to look like Greenham Common without the women.

'How long must it stay in those barrels?' she asked.

'Ought to be eight years.'

'*I can't wait eight years.*'

'Putting it another way, a month or two.'

The season wheeled, and the orchard at Edgar's Farm was burdened with russet apples. Since the press existed it was used. To the apple-core mountain were added fresh dribbling foothills.

It was doing them a favour to take some of it away.

Dan borrowed the blacksmith's van and Lady Simpson's shovel and some plastic feed-bags and Mary Cousins, and they brought their raw material back to the distillery at four in the morning.

Mary bought the yeast, from a chemist near the library. She said her uncle was taking up wine-making. She blushed, because she had no uncle and she was unaccustomed to lying.

Dan borrowed large kitchen coppers from the pantries of nobs for whom he pretended to work. He and Mary filled the coppers with mash, and added yeast as the instructions directed. Mary had the use of her brother's Mini while he was abroad. She used it to come and sniff the fermenting apple-sauce. It made her feel drunk and amorous. She was freckled by the autumn sun. She was having the time of her life. She thought she was the only assistant librarian in the country acting as assistant distiller to a poacher in the woods.

While the apples were fermenting they tried the still.

They found a few places where steam leaked out. They plugged them. Crazy as it looked, uneconomical as it was, the still worked: the material did boil, the steam left the still at a temperature measured by the thermometer, the water did cool it in the coil of the condenser, and it did arrive as clear fluid in the receiver. The difficulty was to keep the fire under the still exactly right—the temperature of the steam had to be kept within a narrow band. Too high, and too many impurities went with the alcohol into the condenser; too low, and the less volatile congenerics did not go with the alcohol to flavour it; too high or low and you made stuff that sent you blind or mad.

Dan devised a system of metal plates to slide under the still to conduct away excessive heat; he borrowed a pair of bellows from Mrs Calloway, for whose small open fire they were absurdly large. By keeping his oven fed with small dry wood, and by alternate use of bellows and bafflers, Dan found he could keep the steam at a pretty level temperature.

They needed days of bright sunshine, to make the fire invisible. Luckily there were plenty of those that autumn.

Mary was owed a week's holiday. She did not go abroad or to Scotland. She gave her Milchester landlady a rambling account of the scientist she was helping with his experiments, and her parents on the telephone a description of the ecologist she was helping with his fieldwork. She was pretty truthful— she described Dan accurately.

It was possible, with simple chemistry, to measure the alcohol content of the fermenting mash. It was possible to do so by nose, too. The stuff would have knocked a cart-horse over. The moment had come.

Dan tended the fire, while Mary ladled tipsy apple-sauce into the still. The flames were almost white. There was no smoke. Dan used Mrs Calloway's bellows. They waited hand in hand for the first bubble. Dan watched the thermometer and Mary added to the pile of wood stacked by the oven.

They heard the first porridge-like gurgle as the alcohol began to boil.

Tending the fire in relation to the thermometer now became and remained crucial. The thermometer showed a tendency to go up and down like a yo-yo. Not hot enough—more fuel—bellows . . . Getting too hot—slide the plates under the still . . . Buckets of cold water from the well ready to top up the coolant . . . Hardly time to hold hands, no time to kiss anybody, was it worth it, could anything be worth that?

And the first drop of the first distillation arrived in the receiver: not with a plop or a tuck of drums, but faintly visible as a glossy ghost at the bottom of the jar.

'Applejohn,' said Mary, awed as though by the appearance of a spirit even more divine.

They kept the mash simmering until every drop had evaporated that boiled below the critical temperature. Mary was scarlet in the face. Sometimes she gave little shouts of excitement and triumph.

They emptied and refilled the still, and boiled up a new lot. Slowly the level rose in the receiver. The rise was imperceptible if you watched; you learned to turn away for as long as you could bear it, and then look again. The third day it rained; they huddled under a cover borrowed from a straw-stack, and screened their fire from snoopers.

Among the nobs who employed him, Dan caused it to be put about that he was suffering from the gallopen gargles, a condition which required only rest and quiet. He was embarrassed by the get-well cards and bunches of grapes that arrived at the cottage, but his mother liked the grapes.

Mary prattled to her landlady at night about experiments, and to her parents about field-work.

On the fifth day they poured the spirit back into the still and distilled it a second time. There was significantly less product, because less water. The alcohol content was higher than that of any spirit sold commercially.

All the week they laboured every daylight hour, until at last both sherry-barrels were full, tightly bunged, and installed out of sight in the mouth of a rabbit-hole. Containers and contained were all organic, and Applejohn would gradually and ceaselessly change for the better and better. The oak was very slightly porous; there would be slight evaporation, and slight oxidation from seepage of air into the casks. That was all as it should be. Everything was as it should be. They celebrated with their first full night together. Mary felt much unlike an assistant librarian.

She was going back to work in the morning. Dan thought he had better do so, too. He dismantled the apparatus and put the parts in another rabbit-hole. Nobody who found them would know what they were. All the glade where they had worked was haunted by a spirituous fragrance.

Mary went away in midwinter to another job near her family. They both knew their adventure was a kind of lay-by off the main highways of their lives; they both knew they had a friend for ever. Mary would tell Dan where she was, and wherever she was she would come back to taste the first sample of Applejohn. She would have no difficulty finding Dan—he would be where he always was.

Against bottling-day, Dan made a collection of bottles, which he stored in yet other rabbit-holes. The point was the corks. Late-bottled vintage port, Calvados, many liqueurs came in bottles with re-usable corks made airtight by plastic seals. Dan could use sticky tape for a seal, if he was afraid of Applejohn evaporating. He did not think it would be given time to evaporate. He had no difficulty collecting enough bottles—people threw them away— but it had to be done tactfully. Dan Mallett with barrow-loads of bottles took a bit of explaining.

He steamed and scraped all the labels off the bottles. He wrote to Mary, asking for a design for the Applejohn label. Her design was impressive, and contained misleading information. In the centre was a pen-drawing of a gnarled apple-tree after a woodcut by Bewick. Dan was hugely pleased. At her new library Mary made hundreds of photocopies of the label. She sent them to Dan, who bought a pot of glue.

'It's a special kind of wine-tasting,' said Mary. 'It's for charity. Masters of Wine and wine journalists and a Member of Parliament. I don't know how my father got involved. I said I'd go. I said I'd bring a guest. You're the guest. We'll slip in a bottle of Applejohn and see what they say. Expert opinion. We'll *never* have such a chance again.'

'Ought to have another few years in the wood. But it's true we might never have such a chance. I can't go to a party with Members of Parliament.'

'Not in those clothes you can't.'

'Nay,' said Dan in one of his optional voices. 'A-bent meanen t'cam t'sich gatherens wi' me oldie breeches.'

They tapped the barrel which had once held Amontillado. They filled a clear bottle and plugged it with an anonymous cork. Applejohn was almost colourless, with a hint of gold that probably came from the sherry-soaked wood. Some instinct stopped them trying it—a sort of fear. The very first taste of Applejohn would be kept for the experts at the tasting.

They glued the label to the bottle. It looked like a label on a bottle, professional as could be.

The Charity Wine-Tasting was held in a municipal hall of dreadful gloom in the town where Mary's parents lived. Dan borrowed a car to get there. He wore the banker's dark suit which recalled the days of his detested servitude. He had to pay to get in, because it was for charity. Mary introduced him as her friend Mr Mallett, which nobody had ever done before.

There were forty people there, middle-aged and elderly, dressed up smart and talking in hushed voices. There were bottles of wine on tables and trays of glasses. Dan glanced at Mary. She pointed unobtrusively. Applejohn was there.

A man rapped on a kind of lectern and droned something about the work of the charity. Applause. The Member of Parliament droned something about himself. Applause. He was a fat brigadier with purple jowls; he had tasted a lot of wine in his life. The Member said they should get on without further ado to the serious business of the evening. Applause. A man introduced the first wine. Hold it up to the light, sniff, taste. A serious business. Some pompous remarks were exchanged. Dan felt stifled with suspense. Mary was pink with excitement.

One of the experts found the Applejohn. He scrutinised the label. He pulled out the cork and sniffed. Dan and Mary watched him intently, pretending not to do so.

The expert poured a glass for the purple brigadier. The brigadier held it up to the light, sniffed, tasted. He immediately drained the glass.

It was one of those moments which occasionally come at gatherings large and small—a sudden, inexplicable, causeless hush, a focus of all attention on a single happening. Everybody was silent; everybody was watching the brigadier drink his drink.

Already purple, his face blackened. His mouth gaped. He clutched his chest. His knees buckled. He fell heavily, sprawled among the experts.

He was dead. Applejohn had killed him.

The confusion was frightful. Dan lost sight of Mary, who was one of those who had rushed away to find a doctor. He slipped away himself. He supposed his fingerprints were on the bottle. The knock on the door would come in hours rather than days. He wondered drably where they had gone wrong.

In the dawn Dan went to the rabbit-hole which was his brandy-cellar. He rolled out one barrel, and emptied it completely on a tuffet of dead bracken. He emptied the other barrel. He put a match to the brandy-sodden bracken. He burned both barrels. No drop of the lethal stuff survived, to incriminate himself or kill anybody else. The smell was heartbreaking.

The knock on the door.

It was Mary.

'He had a heart-attack,' said Mary. 'He should never have been drinking. He was overweight. They analysed Applejohn. Its proof is much too high but it's absolutely pure. They say it's superb. They drank the whole bottle. Everybody wants to know where it came from. Dan! What's the matter? Why are you crying? *Dan* . . .'

THE BLUDE-RED WINE

ANTONIA FRASER

HE Professor suddenly held up his glass and said something that sounded like 'blood-red'. For a moment, in spite of the odd wording, Jemima Shore thought he was going to propose a toast although he was still seated, and people were still eating their second course. The glass was almost full. Red wine glinted in the light of the branched candlestick in the centre of the table. A dark ruby-red: or blood-red, if the Professor preferred to put it that way.

'The blood-red wine . . . Exactly what kind of wine?' he was asking. It was not a toast. Jemima Shore felt a quick pang of relief. According to the printed programme in front of her, she was due to make her own speech—proposing the toast of the college—immediately after the Queen's health had been drunk. No toast meant no speech, or at least not yet. After-dinner speaking was not Jemima Shore's idea of fun. She did not like public speaking very much in the first place, preferring the television screen, the medium for which, as an investigative reporter and presenter, she had after all been trained. After-dinner speaking in particular gave you the whole length of the meal to dread the moment of rising to your feet, notes in hand . . .

That reminded her. Nervously Jemima checked the continued existence of those same notes in her evening bag (pretty but really much too small for this kind of thing). She had been planning her speech for weeks. It would not do to lose hold of it now.

'Chambertin 1976—according to what it says here,' Claire Donahue had picked up the programme and was peering closely at it. She was an old friend of Jemima's from Cambridge days, hence Jemima's presence at this dinner. Claire had been a lecturer at Mallow for several years and was hoping for tenure. She had invited Jemima to speak on the dubious grounds that this would somehow advance her cause. Jemima, now regretting the weak impulse which had led her to agree—why did she always feel so sorry for Claire, for heaven's sake?—took refuge in irritation at the way Claire simply would not wear her spectacles in public. Ludicrous vanity: it could be nothing else. Surely academics were more or less *expected* to wear spectacles.

Look at Claire with that programme barely a centimetre from her pretty pudgy little nose! Remembering the old days, Jemima decided that Claire must fancy someone or other at the dinner table. Paddy Mayall? He was a handsome hunk all right. Not quite what you expected to find at an academic dinner. The woman next but one, pale with long auburn Pre-Raphaelite hair, appeared from the seating plan to be Mrs Mayall. Was it Jemima's imagination or was she gazing at Claire with active dislike? If Jemima's hunch was correct, no wonder. Sweet little Claire could be surprisingly predatory on occasion.

Marie Mayall . . . what did she know about her? She had received a preliminary gossipy briefing. Ah yes, money, that was it. Her Laura Ashley dress hardly indicated an enormous income. On the other hand, a plain or plainish woman with an exceptionally handsome husband did sometimes indicate the presence of money in the contract . . . Professor Alec Redding, seated on Jemima's left, interrupted these uncharitable thoughts.

'You do realize, my dear Claire, that I am this year's President of the Wine Committee? So that I am well aware not only that this is a Chambertin but also of its precise year, since I chose it myself. I hardly need reminding . . .' Pompous beast, thought Jemima, transferring her irritation to the Professor. She remembered Claire telling her that he had a reputation as a womanizer, students included, since his wife's death a few years back. That and an ostentatious taste for the good things of life, wine, even rather improbably fast cars, no wait a minute, *vintage* cars. Long-delayed adolescence! Well, he would have to do better than that to fascinate her.

The Professor boomed on: 'But then how could you be expected to remember a little detail like the name of the President of the Wine Committee? Matters of greater import on your mind, no doubt.' Greater import— what did that mean? It sounded like a swipe at Claire's private life. Perhaps she had at some point turned down the bouncy Professor. Or was it just heavy-handed academic teasing? Jemima was aware that Alec Redding was still holding up his ruby-red—or blood-red—glass. Time to catch up with Claire's *amours* later when the dreaded speech was over; Jemima was to be the guest of the college for the night. Now what was he saying?

'What *kind* of wine did the King serve? That is my precise question which I have at last happily been able to express.' The Professor paused and then intoned in a suitably sonorous voice with more than a trace of Scottish accent:

> 'The King sat in Dunfermline town
> Drinking the blude-red wine . . .'

The Professor was a smallish man—if his reputation was correct, perhaps he had a short man's compensatory desire to act the lady-killer—but his head at least was impressively leonine. Now he gazed about him as though in triumph at having at last secured an audience. He proceeded to recite the next lines of the ballad, his Scottish accent becoming progressively broader:

> 'O where will I get a gude sailor
> That'll sail the ships o' mine . . .'

'The tragedy of Sir Patrick Spens,' commented Jemima politely. She was aware of some kind of awkwardness in the atmosphere without knowing exactly where it was focused; knowing and loving the ballad from childhood, she was happy to intervene.

> 'To Noroway, to Noroway
> To Noroway o'er the foam'

recited Jemima (but without attempting a Scots accent),

> 'The King's daughter of Noroway
> 'Tis thou must bring her home.'

'Exactly!' Professor Redding beamed at her; for a moment Jemima did glimpse his charm. There was indeed something quite boyish about him, now that he had dropped his pomposity on the subject of the Wine Committee. 'Sir Patrick Spens it is. And what a tragic tale, eh? A lesson for us all. One moment there he was drinking the blude-red wine in Dunfermline town with the King and all. The next moment he had foolishly set off: to bring back his master's bride. Only to bump into a spot of bad weather on the way home. Weather rather like tonight, I fancy!'

It had been an unusually storm-tossed October; persistent rain had made it virtually impossible for Jemima to glimpse anything of the university town as she drove through. The setting of Mallow was said to resemble that of Stratford, with its mediaeval bridge under which flowed another rather less famous river Avon. If the weather cleared up, Jemima might inspect the charms of Mallow properly in the morning. In the meantime the Professor was intoning once more:

> 'They hadna been a league, a league
> A league but barely three
> When loud and boisterous grew the wind
> And *gurly* grew the sea.'

The Professor gave due Scottish relish to the whole passage, but the word 'gurly' in particular caused him to roll his tongue round it with zest. 'And so they all drowned,' he finished with a flourish. 'That's for setting off after a glass or two of red wine.'

'What is your point exactly, Alec?' The middle-aged rather plump lady in the black crêpe evening dress had a formidable air; her spectacles at least were firmly on her nose. Jemima consulted her seating plan. Ah yes, formidable indeed. This was the celebrated Dr Elena Kirkus: the mere sight of her name at the head of a review was enough to send aspiring young scholars' hearts into their boots. 'Apart from letting us all admire your Scottish accent, an unsuspected talent, I must admit.'

'Elena! Now you think I'm trespassing on your literary territory, I can see. Would I do that? *Far* too frightened; look what happened to poor Paddy here. But enough of that. What is my point, you ask. *No* point. No point at all.' The Professor lowered his glass at long last. 'I was merely seeking instruction. What kind of wine would they have been drinking in fourteenth-century Scotland? As a wine buff, I am always full of curiosity on these arcane matters.'

'French wine, of course, imported French wine,' said Paddy Mayall after a pause. 'If not exactly Chambertin. I congratulate you on this, by the way, Alec. And the Pouilly-Fuissé earlier, for that matter.' Paddy Mayall cleared his throat. Jemima had the impression he was speaking slightly reluctantly.

'And so a fourteenth-century Scottish King drank French wine!' Professor Redding sounded even more jovial now that he had at last got the answer to his question. He sipped at the wine in question.

Paddy Mayall looked in the direction of Dr Kirkus. His expression was almost apprehensive. Since she said nothing, he cleared his throat again and continued: 'Thirteenth century, by the way, not fourteenth. The ballad may be based on the voyage of a Scottish princess who went to marry the King of Norway in 1281 . . . Margaret of Scotland . . . King Eric . . . a good many of her train did drown on that occasion . . .' Now Paddy Mayall began to warm to his theme. 'People do sometimes think in error that it was her daughter, the so-called Maid of Norway. Now she *did* die on her way back to Scotland—1290, I think you'll find—but there was no drowning involved . . . so that on the whole the evidence does suggest . . .'

To her shame Jemima's attention began to wander away during this little lecture, back to the ever-present anxiety of her speech. So that she missed the immediate preamble to the incident which followed, while witnessing the drama itself. What Jemima saw was the auburn-haired Mrs Mayall picking up her own wine glass, full or full enough, of red wine, and throwing the contents across the table at the Professor. His white shirt front—like most of the men present, he was wearing a dinner jacket—suddenly revealed an enormous dark red stain; it looked as if he had been shot in some melo-dramatic amateur theatrical. Nor did Mrs Mayall's accompanying words exactly undo this impression.

'That's for your bloody red wine!' she shouted, in an unmistakably genuine Scots accent. Then Marie Mayall scrambled to her feet and half-ran, half-stumbled from the high table and out of the dining hall.

Professor Redding, mopping his shirt with his handkerchief—which merely ruined the latter without cleaning the former—was left exclaiming in what sounded like genuine amazement: 'What did I say? What did I do?'

Paddy Mayall, his handsome face flushed with embarrassment, got up, sat down again, and began: 'Alec, I'm frightfully sorry—' Of those other diners near enough to have taken in what occurred, Claire Donahue kept repeating

'Oh God' in an apparently helpless manner, followed by: 'Should I? Should I go after her, do you think?' But she sat still, Jemima noticed, and she noticed also that Paddy Mayall had fixed Claire with an uncommonly determined stare. No, Claire was not to follow.

It was left to Dr Kirkus to say with dignity but in a voice of unmistakable reproach: 'Alec, how could you? How could you be so tactless? Even cruel. And I thought you were fond of poor Marie.'

Marie Mayall did not come back. A series of the diners at the high table left the hall during the rest of the meal with, Jemima suspected, the intention of persuading her to return. That might have been arguably less embarrassing than the sight of her empty place, especially since the college servants continued to plonk down portions of food there, before removing them untouched. Unlike the excellent wine, the food was rather tasteless; there was also a remarkable number of courses—or was it just the thought of the speech ahead which made Jemima feel the meal was endless? On the other hand who could tell how Marie Mayall would have behaved if she *had* chosen to return. . . . Her face during her outburst had exhibited a degree of passion quite surprising in a woman at first sight shy and even withdrawn beneath her curtain of long loose hair.

Paddy Mayall was the first to leave the hall, when his wife showed no sign of coming back. He came back a short while later without public comment. But he arched his eyebrows in the direction of Claire, who as Jemima's sponsor, was seated on her left. (Mallow did not necessarily alternate the sexes in its high table seating plan, considering that to be an old-fashioned formality.) Jemima thought that this time Paddy Mayall was silently commanding Claire to go after his wife, as previously he had adjured her silently to stay. Sure enough, Claire murmured in Jemima's ear: 'Marie's awfully highly-strung, as no doubt you've noticed. She's probably lurking in the Ladies in floods of tears.' And she too left the hall.

Ten minutes later, Claire returned alone. Professor Redding was the next one to go, and stayed away longest: his shirt, sopping wet and still pinkish in part, showed signs of a prolonged but clumsy repair job when he came back. There was a little extra buzz of conversation from the students in the body of the hall at his return.

'Serve him right, the little stoat,' said a student sitting at the table directly below, loud enough for Jemima at least to hear. The wine-throwing incident had certainly not passed unremarked, if its cause was not understood. For one thing, Jemima Shore's presence at the dinner—a face so familiar from television—concentrated attention upon the high table. Opinions varied, and were hotly argued on both sides, as to whether she looked older/ younger/sexier/not so sexy as she did on the box. (Jemima might have been wryly amused to learn that not one single person speculated as to what she might be about to say in her speech.)

Of Jemima's immediate neighbours, Dr Kirkus was the last to depart and the last to come back. She took the opportunity of the brief break before the speeches to stump from the hall, a heavy but dignified figure. Dr Kirkus was the one to sort out the errant Mrs Mayall, if anyone could: of all those present, she exuded moral authority. But her mission too was unsuccessful. She simply handed Paddy Mayall a piece of paper.

'Marie's gone home,' said Dr Kirkus. 'She left this for you.'

Jemima watched Paddy Mayall unfold the note and then crumple it: this time he reddened with what looked like anger. Jemima felt Claire's attention wandering away from her. They were supposed to be discussing the question of depth in television documentaries: it was already a slightly artificial conversation because Jemima was by now beginning to rehearse her speech in her mind. Since she would touch on the same subject, she was reluctant to pre-empt her arguments in advance.

Paddy Mayall's mouth framed the words: 'Marie's taken the car.'

'My God,' exclaimed Claire aloud, interrupting Jemima's polite response about viewers' attention span. 'I just hope that she's going to be OK driving.'

'Had she drunk so much? I rather thought the famous glass was full,' Jemima added drily.

'Normally Marie doesn't drink, so she drives home. I don't know about tonight. She was in such an odd state. But it's a terrible road at the best of times, and in this weather! Dark and very twisty. Miles away from Mallow— they really shouldn't live so far out, but Marie insisted—' In her nervous state, Claire was beginning to babble.

There would be a time for all this, Jemima decided when the famous speech was safely accomplished. One way or another it could not be long now.

How would she start? '*Professors*, Ladies and Gentlemen'—sudden panic, how many professors were there actually present beyond Professor Redding? She must find out at once. Jemima began to search the seating plan earnestly for academic titles and for the time being forgot about Marie Mayall.

It was in this manner that she did not learn what it was that had upset Paddy Mayall's wife so much until some time after the dinner was over. Elena Kirkus told her about it all as they gathered in the Senior Common Room after dinner for coffee and further drinks. Jemima by now felt the unnatural *bonhomie* of one who has been reprieved from execution—or rather, has been executed and found it did not hurt. Although her speech had been neither the best nor the worst she had ever made—after all that—it was, thank heaven, over. (And she must remember to accept no such nerve-racking invitations from old friends in future, she told herself sternly.)

'You see, poor Marie actually *comes* from Dunfermline,' Dr Kirkus was explaining. 'Or more to the point, her father did. He was the man who built up all those stores from scratch. What are they called? Dunfermline Mac-gregor, something like that.' She mentioned the name of a famous Scottish chain. Money! Yes indeed, thought Jemima, there must certainly be plenty of that about in Marie's family.

'You could certainly call him a king in modern terms. In any case all that was really very close to home, the wine, the drowning and the rest of it. For a clever man, Alec can be *remarkably* imperceptive.' Dr Kirkus frowned; Jemima had a sudden vision of what it must be like to present an ill-prepared essay to Dr Kirkus.

'The drowning—' Jemima prompted her. With her speech over, she found her curiosity about her fellow-diners resurging.

'It made banner headlines at the time. A guest who drank too much and drowned on his way home. The party was at Marie's father's place on or near a river in Scotland. A bridge featured, I know that. Too much was drunk all round, whisky as well as wine, no doubt, but everyone remembered the wine because the young man who drowned had a bottle of wine with him in his car. He had taken it from the house. There was some sort of crash before the drowning, so that there was wine, red wine, everywhere when the police found him. And blood. Mixed.' She paused. 'I'm afraid that particular detail sunk into the public consciousness. The blude-red wine, as Alec so unfortunately phrased it.'

'No wonder she was upset.'

'Marie's father was much criticized at the time—and afterwards—for letting the young man go, let alone take a bottle of wine. I think the whole matter preyed on his mind. He died not long afterwards. The position he had built up—all lost as he saw it. Marie inherited everything of course.' Dr Kirkus sighed.

'Was he really so much to blame?'

'Who can tell? Difficult to control the young. *We* know that all right,' she gestured round her, although there were in fact no students present in the Senior Common Room. 'It wasn't helpful that the young man had been a kind of suitor of Marie's, I gather, and the old man didn't like him very much.' Another sigh. 'But Alec of all people to bring that up! He is very interested in wine, we all know that; rather boringly so, sometimes, dare I say it? But that was carrying an interest altogether too far. Alec—whom I had seen as Marie's protector in a way, since his own wife died, or at least supporter. In her not altogether happy situation. I'm sure you understand what I mean.' Dr Kirkus looked significantly towards Claire and Paddy, now having a conversation in the other corner of the room, which was all too visibly intimate. Claire looked particularly pretty, animated; she had the air of persuading Paddy to something.

'Marie and Paddy married shortly after her father's death. He was a postgraduate student up there: that's his field, Scottish studies of sorts. Too

130

soon perhaps for either of them. It meant that Marie never went on with her own work: a pity, there's a proper intelligence there. And they really are such different characters. She's very reserved: that wine-throwing, so public, is quite a new departure. As for Paddy, I'm fond of him, but I've come to the conclusion his mind is essentially lightweight.'

For all the pleasantness of her tone, Dr Kirkus did not fail to make it clear that the word 'lightweight' was, in her vocabulary, one of extreme moral disapproval. Inwardly, Jemima quailed: that kind of judgement took her back all too rapidly to Cambridge and certain dons she had known there. Had her speech been lightweight, she wondered? Could anything to do with television be other than lightweight in the opinion of Dr Kirkus (who had, by the way, alone among the diners, not congratulated Jemima upon her performance)?

'I had to reprove Paddy just a little in a review in *Literature* once—' Elena Kirkus smiled reminiscently; her gentle smile was really more terrifying than her frown, Jemima decided. Dr Kirkus looked round her. 'Alec Redding, now, with all his faults, there's a first-rate mind. As for your young friend—'

They were interrupted by Claire herself. 'Paddy's taking my car,' she announced swiftly. 'It's ridiculous for him to get a taxi to go all that way to that remote place at this time of night, even if he could. And of course he must go and see if Marie's all right. No, don't be silly, Paddy. How could I possibly need it myself? I'm here with Jemima till dawn, aren't I, discussing the good old days. Everyone drives my car. Everyone except Alec: he's too snobbish about cars.'

'Too knowledgeable maybe: not always the same thing.' It was Dr Kirkus in her tart way who came to Alec Redding's defence, as though regretting her earlier attack. The Professor himself remained silent.

But Claire rattled on regardless: 'Oh go on, Paddy, take it.'

How elated she was! And Claire's careless generosity with her possessions reminded Jemima of the vivid girl she had known at Cambridge: there was something voluptuous about such generosity as though Claire was secretly signalling: 'Have me too.' Jemima was to remember that elation further on during the evening when Claire outlined in private a less than happy situation. The words, both sad and sadly familiar, tumbled out.

'She simply doesn't understand him, she can't seem to make an effort— that awful wine-throwing was about the most positive thing I remember Marie *doing* in public. She's silent most of the time. No one knows what she's thinking—' And so on and so on.

At the same time another picture was emerging, a picture of a large comfortable country house, way beyond any don's salary, situated in a picturesque Mallow country village, far from the bustling university town. Here lived a withdrawn and wealthy woman and her good-looking unfaithful husband; and as far as Jemima could make out, there was no real sign of this ménage, happy or unhappy, coming to an end. The ugly—or encouraging—word divorce was not mentioned by Claire at any point, she noted.

At one point Claire even said: 'Sometimes I hate him! I wish he was dead. No, I wish *I* were dead. It's just that I hate him for being so weak: he'll never leave her, her and her lovely money. Oh forget it, Jemima. I think I'm rather drunk.' She had indeed polished off most of a bottle of red wine, no Chambertin this, but some rougher vintage designed for late-drinking when it headed in the general direction of oblivion. Jemima herself drank one glass and stopped.

So it could hardly have been the wine which gave her such disturbed dreams and half-waking reflections; perhaps it was the tension still lingering from her speech on the one hand and an unexpectedly fraught social evening on the other. In particular the lines of the old ballad began to weave through her brain in zany fashion, rearranging themselves in new patterns:

> The Professor held up his blude-red wine
> O who will answer this question of mine?

Other lines came back to her: the ominous presage to Sir Patrick Spens' journey when his servant had seen 'the new moon with the auld one in her arms'. A doomed expedition; she began to drift again and the lines drifted with her: 'the new woman with the old man in her arms ... O who will answer this question of mine?'

When Jemima did wake up to the urgent pleading summons of Claire Donahue, the latter's ravaged face and desperate cry seemed to come straight out of her threatening dream.

'He's dead,' she was saying, 'Oh Christ, how shall I bear it? What shall I do? He's dead—'

'Of course he's dead,' muttered Jemima stupidly; she was still within the ballad's nightmare. 'Sir Patrick Spens is dead.' Luckily Claire did not seem to hear her.

'Paddy,' she was wailing over and over again. 'Paddy, oh Paddy.'

Throughout the day which followed, Jemima saw it as her duty to remain in Mallow: it would hardly be honourable to depart hastily for London in the wake of such a ghastly tragedy. Besides, she could support Claire. The details of Paddy Mayall's death gradually emerged. None was pleasant. First, it transpired that he had crashed his car—Claire's car—through Mallow's historic medieval bridge and into the Avon below. The car appeared to have gone out of control, or else he had taken the bridge too fast in the darkness. He had then drowned in the fast-flowing storm-swollen river—perhaps he had hit his head first and been knocked unconscious—but that was not yet known for certain. All that was bad enough. Worse was to follow in the afternoon.

'The police,' Claire said in a dull voice, tears temporarily stilled. 'The police have been to see me. Because it was my car: the car he was driving, the car that crashed. They think it may have been tampered with, fixed in some way. The brake linings were virtually severed and then—he didn't get very far, did he?' She was beginning to tremble again. 'I don't understand about cars, but I wasn't careless about *that* kind of thing, it had only just come back from the garage. If someone did it on purpose, who on earth would want to kill *me*?' Claire ended on a piteous note.

Then she gasped. 'Oh my God, are they suggesting *I* killed Paddy?' She began to weep again. 'How could they believe that? How could anyone? He should never have been driving. If only Marie hadn't run off like that, if only Alec hadn't got going on the subject of his stupid bloody wine, oh curse him for it—that started the whole thing off—'

'Wait a minute.' The haunting images of the night were beginning to re-form in Jemima's mind, at first in spite of herself, and then in a more purposeful fashion. 'O who will answer this question of mine?' She let the images have their way. She began to see what an answer to the question might be.

It was Dr Kirkus to whom she posed it. She found the older woman seated in the college library in front of a large open book; but her attitude indicated mourning rather than her reading; her spectacles lay useless beside the book.

'I was very fond of Paddy.' Her manner was composed as ever. 'Light-weight maybe in intelligence, but yet—' She stopped. For once Dr Kirkus appeared to be at a loss how to go on. Jemima took the opportunity to ask her a question.

Other questions and other answers would follow. The police would later fill in all the grisly details of the truth in their patient, relentless and, on the other whole, admirable manner. But before that process could get under way, Jemima had to put her own question.

'Why did you ask me?' Dr Kirkus looked steadily at her.

'You have a first-class mind.' Jemima's smile was not without irony. She added, 'And besides, you know them.'

'Yes,' said Dr Kirkus after a long silence. 'It could have happened like that. It would have been in both their characters. Certainly what seemed outwardly to take place was not in either of them. So the evidence suggests—' She paused to assume her spectacles. 'I was very surprised by Alec even at the time, and even more surprised by Marie.' It was a judgement, the first judgement but not the last, on Professor Redding and his mistress, Marie Mayall, for the murder of her husband Paddy.

When you looked at the events of the previous night from another angle, thought Jemima afterwards, how simple they seemed: planned with the same determination as her own speech, but with none of the same reluctance. A clever man, sexually active, with a taste for high living, determined to marry his less intelligent colleague's wealthy wife; the fact that the aforesaid colleague had not the sense to be faithful but actively philandered with a member of the same college was simply an added bonus. With Marie—reserved but passionate—in his thrall, it was easy for Alec Redding to devise his own very public insult: then Marie's carefully-coached response followed, which got her away from the dinner and home to safety in her own car.

The inevitable offer of another car—Claire's car—came next: inevitable because Claire famously lent out her car, and since she was due to spend the night talking to her old friend, she would scarcely need it herself. Redding's stained shirt was then the perfect excuse for him to leave the hall and fix the brakes . . . Redding, who was 'snobbish' but also 'knowledgeable' about cars . . . As for the brakes, supposing suspicion fell afterwards: where was it likely to fall but on Claire herself? Claire who was jealous of her lover's refusal to leave his rich wife.

'I wish he were dead,' Claire had told Jemima in a fit of drunken despair. Might not she have told others the same story?

Even if that accident had failed, the blood—the blood red as wine—of Paddy Mayall would have flowed sooner or later. The new woman was to have the old man in her arms. Paddy Mayall's tragedy had been ordained as surely as that of Sir Patrick Spens, even if it was less noble.

SONG FOR VINTNERS

LORD ALFRED DOUGLAS

The Lion laps the limpid lake
   The Pard refuses wine,
The sinuous Lizard and the Snake,
   The petulant Porcupine,
Agree in this, their thirst to quench
Only with Nature's natural drench.

In vain with beer you tempt the Deer,
   Or lure the Marmozet;
The early morning Chanticleer,
   The painted Parroquet,
Alike, on claret and champagne
Gaze with unfaltering disdain.

No ale or spirit tempts the Ferret,
   No juice of grape the Toad.
In vain towards the 'Harp and Merit'
   The patient Ox you goad;
Not his in rapture to extol
The praises of the flowing bowl.

The silent Spider laughs at cider,
   The Horse despises port;
The Crocodile (whose mouth is wider
   Than any other sort)
Prefers the waters of the Nile
To any of a stronger style.

The Rabbit knows no Private Bar,
   The Pelican will wander
Through arid plains of Kandahar,
   Nor ever pause to ponder
Whether in that infernal clime
The clocks converge to closing time.

True 'bona-fide traveller'
 Urging no sophist plea,
How terrible must seem to her
  Man's inebriety;
 She who in thirsty moments places
 Her simple trust in green oases.

 With what calm scorn the Unicorn,
  In his remote retreat,
 Must contemplate the fervour born
  Of old Château Lafite.
 Conceive the feelings of the Sphinx
 Confronted with Egyptian drinks!

from Tails With a Twist, 1979

MEMORABLE
MEALS

ON DINING ALONE

M. F. K. FISHER

LUCULLUS, the Roman host whose dinners are still talked about for their elaborate menus and their fabulous cost, grew tired one day of dining with other men.

He ordered a meal for one person. When it was served to him, he was conscious of a certain slackness: the wine was perhaps a shade too cold, and the sauce for the carp, which certainly was less succulent than usual, lacked that tang for which his chef was justly famed.

Lucullus frowned and summoned the major-domo.

'Perhaps, perhaps,' that official agreed, with a flood of respectful salutations. 'We thought that there was no need to prepare a fine banquet for my lord alone——'

'It is precisely when I am alone,' the great gourmet answered, icily, 'that you require to pay special attention to the dinner. At such times, you must remember, Lucullus dines with Lucullus.'

At such times few men realize that they are dining with themselves. In fact, they try to forget that rather frightening truth. They read the newspaper or turn on the radio if they are at home. More often they flee from themselves to friend-filled clubs, or to the noisiest nearest restaurant, where other lone humans eat crowded together in a hungry, ugly mob and take digestive pills between their hurried courses.

It is a pity. An occasional meal with himself is very good for Mr Doe. It gives him time to look about him; quiet in which to savour his present mouthful; opportunity to broil his steak a new way or try again those dishes his wife hates.

He need not take it too seriously, however. Old Thomas Walker, The Original, whose preoccupation with the fine points of dining approached pomposity at times, declared himself thus on the problem:

When dining alone is necessary, the mind should be disposed to cheerfulness by a previous interval of relaxation from whatever has seriously occupied the attention, and by directing it to some agreeable object.

The 'interval of relaxation' might well be used for broiling a tender filet, although I doubt if Mr Walker meant just that; and there could be no more 'agreeable object' toward which to direct attention than a fine little bottle of red wine from the Côte d'Or. There with a leaf or two of salad and some crusty sour-dough bread, Lucullus has a meal fit even for Lucullus.

An Englishman, however, and an earl at that, once mapped out a slightly more complicated menu.

'A good soup [he said], a small turbot, a neck of venison, ducklings with green peas or chicken with asparagus, and an apricot tart—it is a dinner for an emperor.'

Perhaps he was right, Louis XIV of France, who always dined alone at one o'clock, ate several soups, three solid courses, and then dessert.

He also ate only from a square table, and was served by nobles of his court, both facts probably influencing his digestion to a certain extent. (Many people enjoy good food only to the sound of soft music, or in a room with black walls. My mother cannot swallow if a cat is near her. Hunger, I observe, is not a part of these equations.)

I have known two people who understood, and probably without one thought about it, why Lucullus dined with Lucullus. One was an old man, the other a girl of sixteen and usually inarticulate.

Biddy was tall and quiet, with magnificent brown eyes and the stiff awkwardness of a new-hatched butterfly. She lived in a kind of doze, seemingly placid, lethargic, docilely stubborn.

One day she took her week's allowance and moved tranquilly and relentlessly towards the tram, muttering of errands and birthdays and such. To her mother's puzzled questions she smiled reassurance, vague but firm.

Late that afternoon she came back.

She brought no birthday presents nor evidence of errands done, but one rather spotted paper bag, from which she drew a long brown cut of *apfelstrudel* for her mother. She was vaguer than usual, but seemed to be unharmed—and the *strudel* was delicious.

Later I saw Biddy. We were talking of restaurants. I saw her eyes flash suddenly when I mentioned Spring Street in Los Angeles, where, one man said, the best and worst food in seven states can be found in fewer than as many blocks.

'I hear you went to town last Saturday,' I said, feeling like Sherlock Holmes and Tom the Peeper. 'What did you do?'

Biddy looked quickly at me, and then smiled rather sheepishly.

'Spring Street, eh? Where did you go?'

'Well—I went to *Katie Levey's*. And why haven't you told me how good it is? And the people!'

'Lots of Austrian Jews, I suppose?'

'Naturally, in a kosher restaurant run by a Viennese! Of course,' she added, carelessly, 'Jews are the best indication of good food in a place.'

I nodded recognition to one of her mother's favourite remarks, and asked, 'But what did you do from eleven to three? You can't eat lunch for four hours.'

Biddy answered me somewhat scornfully: 'I ate breakfast, not lunch, and certainly I ate it for four hours: they understand things like that in a decent restaurant. I drank coffee, with lots of hot milk in it, and ate Viennese tarts and—and things.'

'Things meaning salami and sweet pickles?'

'Mhm.'

She looked dreamily past me. I said nothing, and finally she went on: 'I sat by the cake counter and watched people in the mirror. They were so queer—so *pleasant* at eleven when everybody else in town was rushing around—and especially down there on Spring. And they spoke every language and dipped their tarts in their coffee-glasses.

'Yes,' Biddy exclaimed, 'my coffee was in a glass! It was wonderful!'

Her face was vivid, and in her dark eyes was a quiet awareness I had never seen before. She concluded, almost fiercely: 'Four hours I sat there, watching them dip their bread in coffee-glasses, and thinking. And I'll do it again! It was—it was just what I needed.'

Biddy breakfasted with Biddy, and saw in a mirror clearly, for the first of many times.

The other one who understood was an old man. I never knew who he was. Whenever we went to Victor Hugo's he was there, at a quiet corner table. He was dressed carefully in rather old-fashioned dinner clothes, with his feet in tiny twinkling pumps, like a doll's.

He ate little, and drank a half-bottle of wine with his meat. For dessert he went through a never-varying formula with the intensity and detachment of a high priest.

An avocado was brought to him, cradled in a napkin. He felt of it delicately, smelled it, usually nodded yes. It was cut in two with a silver knife. Then he himself detached the stone-skin from each half, placed one part of the fruit gently on a large plate before him, and sent the other back to the kitchen.

Powdered sugar was brought, and the old man pressed it into the hollow of the fruit. He spent some time over this, making it firm and even.

Next the *sommelier* appeared with a bear-shaped bottle of clear Russian *kümmel*. He poured a generous liqueur-glass of it, waited for the old man's sniff of approval, and went away.

Drop by drop the *kümmel* disappeared into the moon of white sugar, very slowly, very patiently. Very delicately it was stirred and pressed down and stirred again.

Finally the old man ate a small spoonful of the smooth green fruit-flesh, then another. Sometimes he stopped, sometimes he finished it. Then he drank a mouthful of coffee and left.

I have not yet tested his strange dish. I have never been able to construct its flavours for my mind's palate with any clearness. But very clear in my memory is the expression on the old man's face. He was happy as Biddy was happy with her coffee in a glass and her mirror. He was at peace, and aware—aware that Lucullus dined with Lucullus for a reason.

from Serve It Forth, (1937?)

'NEVER ANYTHING SO GOOD AGAIN...'

W. M. THACKERAY

IDINED on a Saturday at the Café Foy, on the Boulevard, in a private room, with a friend. We had

> Potage julienne, with a little purée in it;
> Two entrecôtes aux épinards;
> One perdreau truffé;
> One fromage roquefort;
> A bottle of nuits with the beef;
> A bottle of sauterne with the partridge.

And perhaps a glass of punch, with a cigar, afterwards: but that is neither here nor there. The insertion of the purée into the julienne was not of my recommending; and if this junction is effected at all, the operation should be performed with the greatest care. If you put too much purée, both soups are infallibly spoiled. A much better plan it is to have your julienne by itself, though I will not enlarge on this point, as the excellent friend with whom I dined may chance to see this notice, and may be hurt at the renewal in print of a dispute which caused a good deal of pain to both of us. By the way, we had half-a-dozen sardines while the dinner was getting ready, eating them with delicious bread and butter, for which this place is famous. Then followed the soup. Why the deuce *would* he have the pu——but never mind. After the soup, we had what I do not hesitate to call the very best beefsteak I ever ate in my life. By the shade of Heliogabalus! as I write about it now, a week after I have eaten it, the old, rich, sweet, piquant, juicy taste comes smacking on my lips again; and I feel something of that exquisite sensation I then had. I am ashamed of the delight which the eating of that piece of meat caused me. G—— and I had quarrelled about the soup (I said so, and don't wish to return to the subject); but when we began on the steak, we looked at each other, and loved each other. We did not speak—our hearts were too full for that; but we took a bit, and laid down our forks, and looked at one another, and understood each other. There were no two individuals on this wide earth—no two lovers billing in the shade—no mother clasping baby to her heart, more supremely happy than we. Every now and then, we had a

143

glass of honest, firm, generous Burgundy, that nobly supported the meat. As you may fancy, we did not leave a single morsel of the steak; but when it was done, we put bits of bread into the silver dish, and wistfully sopped up the gravy. I suppose I shall never in this world taste anything so good again.

from 'Memorials of Gormandising', *Fraser's Magazine*, June 1841

I wish for a sheep's head and whisky toddy against all the French cookery and champagne in the world.

Sir Walter Scott: *Letters*

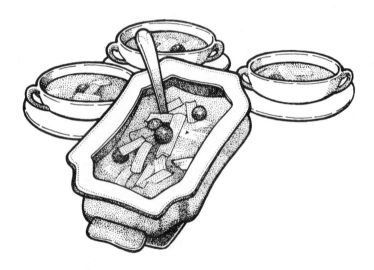

TIT-BIT

AUGUSTUS HARE

TALK of strange relics led to mention of the heart of a French king preserved at Nuneham in a silver casket. Dr Buckland, whilst looking at it, exclaimed, 'I have eaten many strange things, but have never eaten the heart of a king before,' and, before any one could hinder him, he had gobbled it up, and the precious relic was lost for ever. Dr Buckland used to say that he had eaten his way straight through the whole animal creation, and that the worst thing was a mole—that was utterly horrible.*

Recorded by Augustus Hare, 4 June 1882. (*The Story of My Life*, 1896) of William Buckland (1784–1856) Professor of Mineralogy, Oxford, 1813, Dean of Westminster, 1845–56.

---

* Dr Buckland afterwards told Lady Lyndhurst that there was one thing even worse than a mole, and that was a blue-bottle fly. C.R.

LES TROIS COCHONS

JOHN DAVIES M.W.

THREE pigs went to market—in south west France. Originally there were only two, John Salvi, formerly of Sichel & Co, and Martin Bamford, late managing director of Gilbeys in France, both dedicated stomachs who once spent six months preparing for a food tour of Italy, looking up recipes and cooking at each other under the guidance of John's Uncle Aldo, a renowned Italian chef.

They baptised themselves pig, doubtless in some appropriate liquid. 'Hullo pig, this is pig, how are you?' 'Oh fine pig, I had my first *alose* yesterday,' (or asparagus, or *piballes* or lamprey or Cavaillon melon). It was very important to be first in such matters. I came out to Lascombes in the Médoc in 1971, and became an honorary cochon. Sadly Martin Bamford died in 1982. I departed the Médoc, less finally, in 1983 leaving John Salvi in sole possession of the field.

So the period I now recall lasted from 1971 to 1983. All three of us had large houses more or less at our disposal—Bamford at Château Loudenne, Salvi at Château Palmer and I at Château Lascombes—but the real festivals took place in a small cottage (a French lady described it as a *mouchoir de poche*) in the Lot owned by Bamford. Other friends would join us at weekends, notably the late Willie Willshaw, who described one such happening in the *Guardian*. He remarked how equable and polite we three individualists were to each other. 'Could you possibly spare a little of that reduction for my sauce?' 'Oh, I'm afraid I threw that away; I thought it was washing up.' 'Oh never mind old chap, I'll start again.'

The great time was a weekend usually in November or December when game, truffles and foie gras were about. The cottage was only a 'sleeps 3', so rooms in inns were taken and other friends who lived nearby took part in the *consommation*. It required planning. For a simple weekend a visit to the Villeneuve market would do; full of fresh vegetables, enormous loaves of country bread, fat capons and even fatter geese still with their 2lb livers inside them. This took lots of time because Bamford was both an exacting and dilatory shopper.

The gastronomic weekend however required the resources of the great market and food shops of central Bordeaux. Once we attempted saddle of venison with sauce Veneur, which requires that the meat be marinated in wine and aromatics days in advance. I duly ordered it from my little lady in the market. I say mine though in fact we were hers, jealously guarded against rival *vendeuses*. 'C'est mon client!' she would cry as we approached. We put it to steep in a billy can in the Salvi kitchen on the Tuesday before the weekend. By Thursday it had begun to give off smells of extreme putrefaction. Alarmed, I consulted my lady game dealer. She smiled saying 'Ce n'est pas de l'agneau que vous avez acheté, Monsieur.' She was right, it was not lamb that was giving off the overpowering smell that kept us company on our three-hour car journey to the Lot. But the result was perfection; venison that melted in the mouth, pink from the briefest sojourn in the oven.

There was an enormous fireplace in the cottage with a *crémaillère* from which hung an iron pot which we used to make *garbure*, a ham and cabbage soup so thick that the wooden spoon could stand upright in it. Also we would hang woodcock by their necks on string in front of the fire to roast, undrawn, and at a magic moment their interiors would collapse on to waiting bread beneath to make a toast which was the quintessence of game.

A triumph, attempted but once, though in the Médoc rather than the Lot, was the bird within a bird, within a bird, within a bird, immortalised in Vita Sackville West's account of life in Knole in Edwardian times. It took the entire day. We boned a quail and put a truffle surrounded by foie gras inside. This went into a boned partridge, the cavities filled with veal forecemeat, which went into a similarly boned and stuffed pheasant and all into a large boned Barbary duck. When tied, it looked like a football. A stock was made of all the debris, and the ball, wrapped in a cloth, was poached in it. A separate *sauce périgourdine* was made to serve with it.

Sadly the great Willie Willshaw, who originally set up Harvey's restaurant in Bristol, preceded all of us to set up the great *mise en place* in the sky, and we remembered him, with a decent glass of wine of course, but also by recreating his famous pie: quails stuffed with oysters, wrapped in thinly sliced *contrefilet* of beef, and a crust made with little butter but lots of cream.

I haven't mentioned much of the wine we drank. It was never remarkable; since we came across the great wines of Bordeaux during the week we tended to drink the small wines, the Madirans, Côtes de Duras, Jurançon and Bergerac, at the weekend.

We didn't confine ourselves to cooking; it was necessary occasionally to sample the talents of other cooks. Once, we started off at Troisgros (appropriate perhaps) at Roanne where after dinner we fell in with *les frères Troisgros* and some jolly Parisians on their way south, and agreed to meet for breakfast. Naturally nothing as ordinary as coffee and croissants would do. It was *oeufs brouillés aux truffes*, served of course with Brouilly, and St Nectaire cheese with a respectable vintage of Palmer. We finished that trip with a magical lunch at the Auberge de l'Ill at Illhausern in Alsace which ended in the garden at about 6pm. The patron, Jean-Paul Haeberlin, sat with us by the river drawing sketches for us on menu covers.

It was a marvellous period, but one has to have a young strong stomach to stand that pace. As I said at the beginning, three pigs went to market; but it was a French market and there were no tears.

from Sunday Times Wine Club Magazine

FRYING TONIGHT

VERNON SCANNELL

Outside, the dark breathes vinegar and salt;
The lemon window seems to salivate,
Draws peckish kids, black moths to candlelight.

Inside you may sit down to eat, or take
Your parcelled supper out into the night.
On each white halo of a china plate

Dismembered golden dactyls form a nest
About the scab of batter which, when split,
Confesses flesh as white as coconut.

Beneath investigation of bright fork
The naked body breaks and separates,
Unfolds its steaming leaves in smooth soft flakes.

Sleek, plump bottles, bodies almost black,
Hold vinegar on all the table tops
Like little holy sisters in white caps.

And on the counter in a gallon can,
Floating blindly in translucent brine,
Small green dirigibles loll still, becalmed.

Those silver vats behind, they all contain
Hot lakes of oil: when fresh peeled chips are drowned
They spit and sizzle like a thousand cats.

In front a patient congregation stands;
These serious communicants who long
To feel warm parcels solid in their hands

Later, at home, replete, they may spread out
Stained paper cerements, read about old scores
Dead scandals, weddings, unimportant wars.

FROM PARSON
WOODFORDE'S
DIARY ...

APRIL 15 1770. We breakfasted, dined, supped and slept again at home. Brewed a vessell of strong Beer today. My two large Piggs, by drinking some Beer grounds taking out of one of my Barrels today, got so amazingly drunk by it, that they were not able to stand and appeared like dead things almost, and so remained all night from dinner time today. I never saw Piggs so drunk in my life, I slit their ears for them without feeling.

APRIL 16. We breakfasted, dined supped and slept again at home. My 2 Piggs are still unable to walk yet, but they are better than they were yesterday. They tumble about the yard and can by no means stand at all steady yet. In the afternoon my 2 Piggs were tolerably sober.

AUG. 10 1786. Nancy and self very busy this morning in making the Charter* having some Company to dine with us—But unfortunately the

---

* 'Charter' does not appear, to my knowledge, in any standard reference work as the name of a dish. It seems certain to me to be a local, or period, version of 'Chartreuse' 'an ornamental dish of meat or vegetables cooked in a mould' (Oxford English Dictionary Supplement, Vol I). C.R.

Cellar Door being left open whilst it was put in there to cool, one of the Greyhounds (by name Jigg) got in and eat the whole, with a Cold Tongue & c. Sister Pounsett and Nancy mortally vexed at it. Js Clarke and Wife and Jenny Ashford dined and spent the Afternoon with us—We had for Dinner some Maccarel, boiled Beef, a Couple of Ducks rosted, a brace of Pigeons rosted and a Barberry Tart.

JUNE 11 1788. I breakfasted, supped and slept again at home. Nancy breakfasted supped, &c again at home. Betsy Davy breakfasted, supped, & c. here again. About 1 o'clock Mr Du Quesne called here on horseback and I went with him on my Mare to Mr Jeanes's, and Nancy and Betsy Davy went thither also in my little Cart, where we all dined, with Mr and Mrs Jeanes Junr., Mr and Mrs Jeanes Senr., Mr and Mrs Locke ... Miss Short, Mr Charles Springger, ... Mr and Mrs Priest and Miss Mary Priest from Reepham. We had a very excellent Dinner, that is to say, a fine Piece of fresh Salmon with Tench and Eel, boiled Ham and Fowls, the best part of Rump of Beef stewed, Carrots and Peas, a fore Qr. of Lamb rosted, Cucumbers and Mint Sauce, a Couple of Ducks rosted, plain and Currant Puddings. After Dinner 2 large Dishes of Strawberries, some Blanched Almonds with Raisins and Aples. We were much crowded at Table, rather unpleasant. Major Lloyd with his 2 eldest Daughters joined us at the Tea Table in the Evening which made the whole Company then consist of 18 in Number. After Coffee and Tea we had two or three Songs from Miss Kate Lloyd who sings delightfully indeed. It was sometime after 9 o'clock before we got back to Weston—we returned as we went. Upon the whole we spent a very agreeable Day. Mr Jeanes Senr. is a mighty cheerful good natured plain downright Man. Mr Locke a very neat well looking old gentleman, and Country Esq. fond of Hunting, keeps 16 fox Hounds, talks plain Hampshire and Delights also in farming.

JULY 11 1789. I breakfasted, supped and slept again at Cole. Nancy breakfasted, supped and slept again at Cole. Mr Du Quesne breakfasted, supped and slept again at Cole. Sister Pounsett and Daughter, my Niece Nancy and self with Mr Du Quesne dined and spent the Afternoon at Ansford, at Mr Frank Woodfordes with him and his Wife, at Ansford Parsonage the Place and House in which I was born and lived many Years but had not been in it before this day, for almost fifteen years, owing to a disagreement between us, which now I hope will be ever done away. The House and Garden greatly altered for the best. We had a very good Dinner, a fine Piece of fresh Salmon, a Leg of Mutton rosted, fricasseed Rabit, a Couple of Ducks rosted and Peas, a currant Pye and Syllabubs &c. A good Desert of Fruit after Dinner, Strawberries, Cherries and Currants. Mr Frank behaved very hearty and generous to us as did his Wife, who seemed to be very attentive.

MARCH 6 1795. Mr Custance, Mr and Mrs Corbould, and Mr Stoughton of Sparham, dined & spent the Afternoon with us and stayed till after 9 o'clock at Weston Parsonage. We gave them for Dinner a Couple of boiled Chicken and Pigs Face, very good Peas Soup, a boiled Rump of Beef very fine, a prodigious fine, large and very fat Cock-Turkey rosted, Maccaroni, Batter Custard Pudding with Jelly, Apple Fritters, Tarts and Raspberry Puffs. Desert, baked Apples, nice Nonpareils, brandy Cherries and Filberts. Wines, Port & Sherries, Malt Liquors, Strong Beer, bottled Porter &c. After Coffee & Tea we got to Cards, limited Loo, at 1d. per Counter. I won at it abt. 0. 2. 0. It turned out a very indifferent Day of weather as it rained Almost the whole Day, was very sorry for it. All our Dinner was very nicely cooked indeed. Mr Custance eat very hearty for dinner.

The Reverend James Woodforde (b. 1740, d. 1803). His diaries 1750–1802 were published in five volumes from 1924: the editor, John Beresford, published a one-volume selection in 1935. C.R.

... AND FROM
PARSON BEERBOHM'S

[Siegfried Sassoon sent Max Beerbohm a copy of the selection from Parson Woodforde's (1740–1803) *Diary of a Country Parson*, published in 1935. The following from Max's letter of thanks published in *Siegfried Sassoon: Letters to Max Beerbohm*, edited by Rupert Hart-Davis, 1986.]

18 August 1937   *Hotel Bristol, Villars, Switzerland*

My dear Siegfried, August 17 I breakfasted, dined, supped and laid at the Bristol Inn. Florence breakfasted, dined, supped and laid at the Bristol Inn. There is here one Major George Paget, a sour stern man, but we find him very agreeable however. He was in the Army. He asked me if I was a Wiccamist. I said I was an old Chartrousian. He is not a Wiccamist so we have had but little talk together of Winchester. We like him very well. He dined with us at 3 this Aft'noon. The first course was a grand fat Pyke fryed in Honey, a rosted Haunch of Venyzon with Apple Sauce and Oyster Hash over it, 3 young capons boiled in the Swiss fashion, 2 Gooseberry Tarts, and a mash of Turnips. The second course was a round of Cold Beef, Syllabubs, 8 Pig Chops, a Plumb Cake, some Venyzon Pasties, and Veal Soup. We had a Desert of Fruit after Dinner. Oranges, Wallnuts, a Pine Apple, and Apples. There was drank 3 bottles of Omontado, afterwards Beer, Rum and Cyder. We sat long, then went to the Theatre. We had the Front Box, for which I payed 0.1.6. The Play was Irène, a translation of Dr Johnson's Irene, the Entertainment was Florodora. The play was well enough, but the Entertainment not becoming, I wishing it were otherwise. The Major liked the Entertainment well, but not the Play, he having not read it in English, I think. For Supper we had a Dish of Mackarel, a Fruit Pie of Bilberries and Cherries, a great handsome Dutch Cheese, broiled Giblets, a Lobster, tosted Cream Cheese, and Peppered Spinnadge with Mush Rooms. There was drank 2 bottles of Port Wine, 1 of Claret, and 2 bowls of Cold Milk Punch. I then played at Picquett with the Major. I won from him 0.0.3½, but he did not pay me. I will remind him of it if he do not, but think he will. Going to bed I was seized with some spasms of the stomack and hiccupping which I think was caused by the high Mountain Air here. There is snow on the crests of some of the Mountains here in despite of it being August.

O Lord God Almighty, I do beseech Thee to send here more holesome Weather.

August 18. I breakfasted, dined, supped, and laid at the Bristol Inn. Florence breakfasted, dined, supped, and laid at the Bristol Inn. The Major breakfasted, dined, supped, and laid at the Bristol Inn. I felt poorly in my health when dressing and shaving. The Major seemed strong and well in his health. He payed me 0.0.3½. I did not tell him I would have reminded him if he had not payed me. He and I played at Fives against the wall of the Lutheran Chapel. I lost to him 0.0.1¾. I paid him 0.0.1¾. My good horse Joshua that had borne me hither so well from Rapallo with Florence on the pillion has been ill with the staggers. I have dosed him thrice daily with Gin and Onions but this morning he died. I fear I shall not get a better horse than this poor beast, but God's Will be done. We dined at a quarter after 3, the major dined with us. The first course was as prime a haunch of Horseflesh as ever I ate . . .

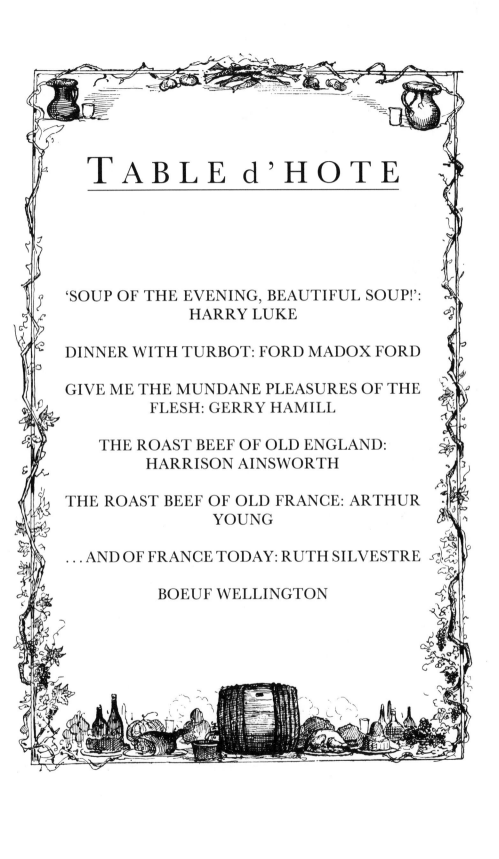

TABLE d'HOTE

'SOUP OF THE EVENING, BEAUTIFUL SOUP!':
HARRY LUKE

DINNER WITH TURBOT: FORD MADOX FORD

GIVE ME THE MUNDANE PLEASURES OF THE
FLESH: GERRY HAMILL

THE ROAST BEEF OF OLD ENGLAND:
HARRISON AINSWORTH

THE ROAST BEEF OF OLD FRANCE: ARTHUR
YOUNG

...AND OF FRANCE TODAY: RUTH SILVESTRE

BOEUF WELLINGTON

'SOUP OF THE
EVENING,
BEAUTIFUL SOUP!'

HARRY LUKE

NATURALLY it is in the Imperial and Royal Courts of pre-austerity Europe that one would expect to find the most complete achievement of variety, in the confection of individual dishes as in the composition of the menu. As regards the former, no other recipe I have seen competes in width of range combined with subtlety of blending with the famous State soup of the Habsburgs. From the time of the Empress Maria Theresa's father Charles VI to that of her great-great-grandson Francis Joseph this masterpiece was offered at the Court Balls of the Hofburg in Vienna and the Royal Castle of Buda, served in the delicate white and gold cups of the Vienna porcelain factory. I append its description as an item of historic no less than gastronomic interest:

The first stocks were made from three kilograms (about 6½ lb) of veal or ham, three kilos of mutton, five or six kilos of venison and other game, roast in butter and then boiled; others were made from eight calves' feet and two cowheels converted into jelly, four white cabbages stewed with three and a half kilos of smoked and fresh pork, two kilos of maize seeds, two kilos of chestnuts, three quarts of lentils, one kilo of pearl barley, and a few French carrots baked with sugar.

When ready, these stocks were laid on ice for four hours, so that every fraction of grease could be removed.

A bouillon was then made from beef and veal bones, mushrooms and other vegetables, and this liquid of a hundred quarts was cleared by the addition of five kilos of hashed beef, two kilos of hashed ox liver, and five litres of white of egg. While the bouillon was boiling it was strengthened by the addition of three cooked fowls (specifically mentioned as 'old'), two ducks, one turkey, four pigeons, five partridges, two pheasants, one goose, and two wild duck.

The concocting of the soup took two days and two nights. The personnel was directed by a first-class Court chef, and consisted of three second-class chefs, three kitchen-maids and three scullions, all chosen for their endurance and conscientiousness since the creation of the various stocks lasted for thirty-two hours without a pause.

The bouillon itself was boiled on a slow fire from eight to ten hours, the stocks and salt being added just before it was ready. When the finished product had been drained through muslin bags it was poured into small cauldrons. These were carried into the ballrooms and transferred to porcelain jugs, from which the soup was poured into china cups for the guests, serving from 1,000 to 2,500 persons.

from The Tenth Muse, 1950

DINNER WITH TURBOT

FORD MADOX FORD

ERHAPS the greatest shock of my career was administered to me during a walk around the Inner Circle of Regents' Park—by Mr H. G. Wells. Mr Wells was prophesying that in the Utopian state you would be able to convert the hat-rack from the hall into mutton-chops or pâté de foie gras. Still more, when perfection was reached, you would be able to carry a week's supply of nourishment in your vest-pocket, in the form of little pellets. But one must have, in addition, a quantity of some bulky non-digestible—not *in*digestible—substance that would pass through the body leaving no nutrition behind it. You would consume that, he said, in order to produce the feeling of distention that forms humanity's chief delight in feeding.

Real Epicureanism has a quality and a poetry as of fugal music. You eat a tiny portion of each of the seven courses of a dinner, not to arrive at repletion, but in order to taste certain flavours in sequence and to be moved by the almost infinite trains of association that will arise in your brain as the tongue communicates to it those savours. Those reminiscences may be exceedingly complex and may range half across the globe.

Thus, Brillat-Savarin, the greatest of all Epicurean writers, wrote that the perfect lunch consists of a *turbot poché au gratin*, a glass of sherry, and a slice of bread and butter. When we degust such a lunch, this is what happens to us: The turbot, that most exquisite of all flatfish, having the consistency and basic flavour of the Rye Bay sole, has above the flavour something equivalent to the bouquet of wine—a faint suggestion of the flavour and perfume of the cucumber. As soon as the first forkful of that turbot spreads its influence on our tongues and palates, we are in a fresh wind on a sparkling sea off Dungeness, the long spit of shingle that has at its end the lighthouse that is the perpetual rival of Griz-Nez light on the cliffs of France.

Deep in the bay, six miles or so from our tossing boat, are the pyramidal red roofs of Rye town. At its top is the house of Henry James. To this house, when he was going down the Channel, George IV used to have himself rowed in a pinnace so as to sleep with a Miss Lamb who was the daughter of the owner of the house.

And it is agreeable, whilst we consume the remainder of our small plate of turbot, to think of the red-cheeked, vast-waisted, first Gentleman of Europe being rowed by his pigtailed bluejackets, each with his black handkerchief in token of mourning for Nelson—passing just by the spot to which the flavour of the turbot has transported us.

We may make the note that the best turbot and the best soles in the world came from Rye Bay. Even in Paris, the home of the *sole Marguéry*, you had to pay double the price that you paid for the soles and turbot taken in the shadow of Griz-Nez light—that is to say, if your Paris fish-monger could have found a Calais fisherman daring enough to poach within the three-mile limit off Dungeness. The *Athena*, a Rye Bay steam-trawler in which I at one time had shares, once made £750 in a single catch of turbot that the captain had the gumption to run over to Calais fish-market at a time when there had been a great shortage of turbot on the French coast.

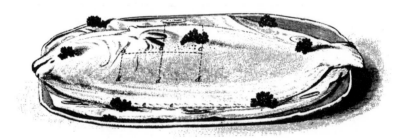

And so we come to the sherry. Nowadays, it doesn't matter what sherry we taste, we think of Algeciras on a day just before the War. They had there, in a little, painted *patio* where you lunched, a little very pale *vino da pasto* that you drank by the thimbleful. That was a really extraordinary experience. Without giving the effect of sourness, that wine must be the dryest of wine dry. It is electric. You feel it run through all your veins like a spark—to the very ends of your toes, the tips of your fingers, and the roots of your hair. And it reduced life to a dream. One understands why the Spaniards say '*La vida es sueño*'—all life is a dream.

In a dream, we wandered that day in Algeciras about the empty, utterly quiet streets of the town. Across the water, Gibraltar confronted us like an image in a dream, and Africa was less substantial even than a cloud. A little, completely naked, jovial boy of two ran about in a shady and deserted alley, stretching out a fat hand and calling: 'Pen . . . nee . . . Pen . . . nee. Give me pen . . . nee.' When we offered him a peseta, he burst into peals of shy laughter and vanished into the black shadows of a stable. That thimbleful of wine had given us the vision of an authentic cherub off the frame of an altar-piece by Murillo. We drifted like incorporeal shades over the blinding expanse of the empty docks in the sunlight that seemed to pour down upon us like the water from a shower-bath. Nor did the dream quality desert us even in the narrow streets of Gibraltar with all the Levantine rock-scorpions and Sinhalese and Moors and Punjabis catching at our elbows and screaming to us.

When we got next day to Malaga, we heard that sixteen men had been killed in Algeciras whilst we wandered in those dream solitudes. It was the beginning of that end.

We have never again come across sherry like that—not even the famous Amontillado of John O'Hara Cosgrave that, in 1842, went twice around the world in the United States frigate *Commodore* could give just that effect. It had more body; it was, as it were, darker in flavour . . . nuttier! But it rather sharpens than stills the intellect.

Our doctor told us that we should never be restored to full health until we should have had at least four months of the *haute cuisine* of France. When we sailed on the *Normandie*, we discussed our first dish with the admirable Monsieur Ozenfant, the chef. One of us thought of *Ailes de Pigeons en Gelèe*— wings of pigeon in aspic . . . and immediately at the mere thought we saw the great studio of Rodolphe and Schaunard in the Boul' Mich'—a vast, dim place furnished with magnificent buhl cabinets, mirrors, tables, and gilt chairs—all painted on the walls, the landlord having seized the other furnishings for rent. Beneath its chandelier, made of a cart-tire hung from the ceiling and garnished with tallow candles, the great crowd of denizens of a Bohemia that has no other seacoast than the Left Bank at the bottom of the Boulevard . . . the great crowd, then, of black-whiskered youths, in peg-top trousers, immense black lavalette cravats, flowing black cloaks and locks, dances with the midinettes of all the Quartier. Their blonde ringlets shake, their little feet twinkle, their little crinolines stand out, their little pantalettes quiver . . . And dancing the schottische, they sing in a little, high unison:

> Et ma jolie colombe qui chante jour et nuit . . .
> And eke my pretty stock-dove sings night and day for me.
> She mourneth for such fair ones as not yet wedded be.
> But I have my fair husband so mourns she not for me.

To which the males in a vast choir shout the refrain:

> Auprès de ma blonde, qu'il fait bon dormi!
> Where lyeth my leman, blonde and warm is she!

And, hearing them over our terrine of pigeon wings in aspic, we saw within that vision another of the French troops, with their shining steel cuirasses, their peaked steel helmets, their ten-foot, shining steel pikes, swinging along between the sunlit, crow-step gables of Holland, the sergeants having great sashes of scarlet satin across their steel cuirasses, the officers in their three-cornered hats with scarlet feathers . . . And, as they swing along, they are singing for the first time that most bittersweet of all the old folk-songs of France—*Auprès de ma blonde* . . .

159

But Rodolphe and Mimi . . . or it may have been Schaunard and Francine with her muff, going home to their attic . . . see on the Boulevard a dove in a cage. It shall, say they in unison, accompany their loves with its cooing night and day. So they dance home, bearing the caged dove and making musical the streets with '*qui chante jour et nuit*'.

I wonder if the young still read Murger's *Vie de Bohème*, which was the Bible of our Paris. It would be a pity if they did not, for you may learn from it more of how to arrange your lives than from a thousand volumes of sermons . . . But then neither do they read sermons . . .

And then we would have Monsieur Ozenfant compound for us one of his matchless *cassoulets de Castelnaudary*, after the fashion of the Inn of the Queen, in the village of that name. Anatole France in *Histoire Comique*, the only one of his books that has much chance of survival, tells you that, in that inn, the kitchen fire has not been out since 1327 and that there has always been a *cassoulet* simmering upon its ashes.

The *cassoulet* was the great dish of all the region from Montpellier to Toulouse—and from Montpellier, France, the dish spread to Montpelier, Vermont, and so to Massachusetts, where, simplified, it became Boston baked beans and pork. In Castelnaudary, they substitute for the pork, slices of goose, mutton, and sausages of foie gras, and, at a given moment before serving, they add purée of tomatoes and grated cheese—the whole quality of the dish being determined by the moment at which you add the purée; because this sauce completely changes its flavour under long baking. And on or under your charcoal fire, the other ingredients of your dish must remain for quite inordinate periods . . . seven hours, ten, fourteen. A day and a half, even.

I saw my grandfather, with the white hair and beard of the King of Hearts, sitting nine feet up in the air in the great hall of Manchester Town Hall—in a Windsor chair on top of nine feet of iron screw, by which, painting at his fresco, THE EXPULSION OF THE DANES FROM MANCHESTER, the painter could raise or lower himself. And the writer, aged ten, looking down at a little farm boy who sat on the floor below the chair, holding up a little pink pig to have its portrait taken by the painter—as part of the loot of the marauding Danes . . .

But when you eat a good *cassoulet*, there is no end to what you may see . . . The Black Prince making his *chevauchée* down through France, leaving a five-mile wide swath of burning farms behind him—burning indeed all Castelnaudary, but leaving the Inn of the Queen because of its beans, its Périgord pasty, and its claret wine. Or the last courts of love, which were holden in the little Alps above that city a month before the hideous Saint Dominic slaughtered all the troubadours. Or Clémence Isaure, in her steeple-crowned hat and trailing, scarlet sleeves, bestowing upon a kneeling bard the first golden rose of her Floral Games . . . But indeed what could you see better than the dim interior of the Inn of the Queen, with the smoke-blackened rafters impending over the twelve tables, each of which holds a great, truffled *pâté de Périgord*—where's your Strasbourg pâté now?—and an immense *cassoulet* still bubbling in its earthenware container . . .

from American Vogue Magazine, (pre 1914)

GIVE ME THE MUNDANE PLEASURES OF THE FLESH

GERRY HAMILL

Give me the mundane pleasures of the flesh,
The roast of sirloin and the Yorkshire pud
With petits-pois and cauliflower afresh,
And lashings of the crisp and golden spud.
Now let the rich brown gravy gently lap
The dab of yellow mustard on the side,
Decant that fruity Châteauneuf-du-Pape,
Which, wed to beef, doth make the perfect bride,
And crowns the very peak of my delight.
Those who would spurn the riches of the earth
—The fasting monk, or spartan anchorite,
With haggard visage and a wasted girth—
Are simply demonstrating that they can
Despise sweet Heaven's gifts to mortal man.

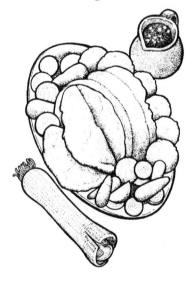

THE ROAST BEEF OF
OLD ENGLAND

KING JAMES THE FIRST DROPS IN ...
HARRISON AINSWORTH

HE KING did ample justice to the good things before him, and especially to the beef, which he found so excellent, that the carver had to help him for the second time. Sir Richard Hoghton ventured to express his gratification that his Majesty found the meat good—'Indeed, it is generally admitted,' he said, 'that our Lancashire beef is well fed, and well flavoured.'

'Weel flavoured!' exclaimed James, as he swallowed the last juicy morsel; 'it is delicious! Finer beef nae man ever put teeth into, an I only wish a' my loving subjects had as gude a dinner as I hae this day eaten. What joint do ye ca' it, Sir Richard?' he asked, with eyes evidently twinkling with a premeditated jest. 'This dish,' replied the host, somewhat surprised 'this, sire, is a loin of beef.'

'A loin!' exclaimed James, taking the carving-knife from the sewer, who stood by, 'by my faith that is not title honourable enough for joint sae worthy. It wants a dignity, and it shall hae it. Henceforth,' he added, touching the meat with the flat of the long blade, as if placing the sword on the back of a knight expectant, 'henceforth, it shall be SIR-LOIN, an see ye ca' it sae. Give me a cup of wine, Master Richard Assheton.'

All the nobles at the table laughed loudly at the monarch's jest, and as it was soon past down to those at the lower table, the hall resounded with laughter, in which page and attendant of every degree joined, to the great satisfaction of the good-natured originator of the merriment.*

from The Lancashire Witches, 1848

---

* 'There is a laughable tradition,' says Nichols, 'still generally current in Lancashire, that our knight-making monarch knighted at the banquet in Hoghton Tower a loin of beef, the part ever since called the sir-loin.' And it is added by the same authority, 'If the King did not give the sir-loin its name, he might, notwithstanding, have indulged in a pun on the already coined word, the etymology of which was then, as now, as little regarded as the thing signified is well approved'—*Nichols's Progresses of James I*, vol. iii.

THE ROAST BEEF
OF OLD FRANCE

EIGHTEENTH CENTURY

IN THE art of living, the French have generally been esteemed by the rest of Europe, to have made the greatest proficiency, and their manners have been accordingly more imitated, and their customs more adopted than those of any other nation. Of their cookery, there is but one opinion; for every man in Europe, that can afford a great table, either keeps a French cook, or one instructed in the same manner. That it is far beyond our own, I have no doubt in asserting.

We have about half a dozen real English dishes, that exceed anything, in my opinion, to be met with in France; by English dishes I mean, a turbot and lobster sauce—ham and chicken—turtle—a haunch of venison—a turkey and oysters—and after these, there is an end of an English table. It is an idle prejudice, to class roast beef among them; for there is not better beef in the world than at Paris.

from Arthur Young: *Travels in France*, 1791 (written before the Revolution)

... AND OF
FRANCE TODAY

'JUST AN ORDINARY SUNDAY LUNCH'

RUTH SILVESTRE

IT IS 12:20 exactly as we drive down to the farm on a sunny morning in south west France. We have already been warned that it is not to be a banquet, just an ordinary Sunday lunch with the family and a few friends. By 12:30 we are part of a leisurely gathering in the flowered courtyard; our neighbouring farmer and his father-in-law, two town cousins and their children, two elderly relatives and the local taxidermist and his ample wife.

In Sunday aprons, our hostess and her mother appear briefly for the ritual kissing, then hurry back to the business in hand. We, after a single aperitif, process expectantly into the dining room on the verandah. We search for our names which have been written hastily on torn scraps of paper and laid in the soup plates. 'Ruht'—Grandma still cannot spell my name. We settle, pick up our napkins and smile at each other.

'*Servez-vous. Servez-vous!*' begs the farmer's wife from the far end of the table. The taxidermist's wife obliges with alacrity. The soup is a thick bisque de crevettes and there are immediate murmurs of approval. Once finished and the plates collected, the first wine is poured. A glass of local red to start and then a Sauternes '76 to accompany the foie gras entier de la maison which follows.

'*Fai calou!*' agree the old folk in patois, mopping their brows and it is indeed hot even for mid-July. The small thick, creamy slices of duck liver are eaten with an intense pleasure and compared favourably with last year's. Next come princely slices of pale orange Charentais.

First sprinkling it with salt, Grandpa eats the melon from the end of his personal folding knife. It is delicious and fragrant and just the thing to cleanse the palate before the next course, a careful arrangement of 'oeufs farci' and curls of saumon fumé on a bed of tiny vegetables in mayonnaise, with which we drink a very dry Côte de Duras '83.

What next, we wonder?

'*Moi je mange trop de pain*' sighs the farmer reaching for yet another slice as Grandma carefully carries in a shallow tureen, steam rising from a dark, aromatic sauce. It is a *civet de lièvre* made from a hare shot by Grandpa last season and the flesh falls from the bones. We drink a red wine from the

165

local Cave Co-operative de Sept Monts at Monflanquin whose Cuvée Special '84 lately gained a Paris gold medal. We, however, are drinking our own special cuvee. It spent four years in an oak barrel which previously held Cahors, and was finally bottled at Easter—when the moon was right. It is very good.

The farmer's wife is now carving a huge roti de boeuf in the kitchen. She piles up the thick slices surrounding them with a quantity of *haricots verts* gleaming with oil and dotted with garlic. Her husband is dusting a hand-made bottle without a label. Eyes widen.

'What is it?'

'*Un vieux Corbières.*' He tries to look nonchalant but fails.

'*Mais, de quelle année?*' The excitement mounts. He shrugs.

'*Je ne peux pas le dire.*' He turns to his father-in-law. '*Quarante-cinq, Quarante huit?*'

Grandpa nods. The Corbières is a dark brownish red. It gleams and is wonderfully smooth and is savoured with reverence. The beef is wonderful too. A town cousin, his chin glistening, asks if it is reared on the farm.

'Of course!' The farmer is proud.

'Don't you mind?' asks one of the children. The farmer shakes his head, smiling at the boy.

After a simple green salad the farmer's wife, to many oohs and oh la las, carries in the *tourtière*, the superb south-west French version of an apple pie. The day before, the tissue thin pastry was resting, covering the entire surface of the double dining table, before being delicately folded over the apple and eau-de-vie de prune and piled up in sculptured curls six or seven inches high. It is Grandma's speciality.

'*C'est une fantaisie*' says Grandma modestly. This tough little lady who can drive a tractor, kill a duck and harvest potatoes with the strongest has little enough 'fantaisie' in her life.

Sorbet de cassis now arrives in its turn followed by bowls of peaches and apricots and we drink our last wine, sweet and golden and also made on the farm. When the coffee is poured from the family Limoges it is almost 4:30 and still the conversation rolls around the table. As we are offered digestifs there are impassioned discussions about the relative merits of Armagnac 'haut' or 'bas' and the town cousin tries the Calvados brought back from a visit to Normandy.

Lunch finally over, we stagger outside. Conversation languishes for a while but soon the boules appear and fierce games are played: English versus French, old versus young, and town against country with many a shout of rage or triumph as minute distances are verified with a measure.

Later some of us stroll through the farmyard to inspect the pigs, the rabbits, quail and pheasants, and on across the fields to admire the lake, newly dug for irrigation. It was so expensive that, in spite of a government grant, the pump must wait until next year. In the next meadow a herd of creamy cows—the beautiful Blancs d'Aquitaine—regard us inquisitively, flicking their tails. We wander back slowly through meadows alive with butterflies and grasshoppers and are about to make our farewells. They look surprised.

'But you can't go now, it's almost time for supper.'

We are staggered. We have only just recovered from lunch. We try to explain that we simply don't think we could eat any more that day. The farmer's wife laughs.

'Wait and see. Now it is cooler. About nine o'clock you'll just feel like a little something.'

It is with a certain sense of *déjà vu* that we once again assemble round the table. We are, however, one short. The taxidermist who has stuffed so many has himself gone home with a *crise de foie* but his rotund wife is already seated, smiling and eager.

We begin again with a delicious beef consommé and miraculously our appetites return. We drink no fine wines, just last year's local red—judiciously watered by everyone. But there are other treats. Roasted guinea fowl on thin garlic-rubbed toast is followed by a dish of cèpes, brown and crisp. The farmer closes his eyes as their perfume reaches him.

'*Ah, ils poussent des bonnes choses dans les bois*' he murmurs.

The cèpes are then compared with morilles, girolles, and a host of other fungi which they are thunderstruck to learn are left largely unappreciated in England.

After bowls of chocolate mousse and *crème Anglaise* we are talking and drinking coffee at midnight with our still beaming host. Well before seven next morning he will be hard at work. He farms over 70 acres with wheat, maize, three huge plum orchards, a vineyard and 60 head of cattle. He does it all with no regular outside help yet he is one of the happiest men I know. But as he always says:

'*Pour bien manger et bien vivre il faut aller dans le Sud Ouest.*'

from The Guardian

BOEUF WELLINGTON

Apropos to something or other, he mentioned: 'When I first went campaigning to Flanders, I remember there was an old Colonel Watson, of the Guards, who said to me, You little know what you are going to meet with. You will often have no dinner at all; I mean, he said, literally no dinners, and not merely roughing it on a beefsteak or a bottle of port wine.' The Duke seemed much amused at such *roughing*.

*   *   *

General Alava told me that when he travelled with the Duke and asked him what o'clock he would start, he usually said 'at daylight'; and to the question of what they should find for dinner, the usual answer was 'cold meat'. '*J'en ai pris en horreur*,' added Alava, '*les deux mots* daylight *et* cold meat!'

from Stanhope: *Notes of Conversations With the Duke of Wellington*, 1831–1851.

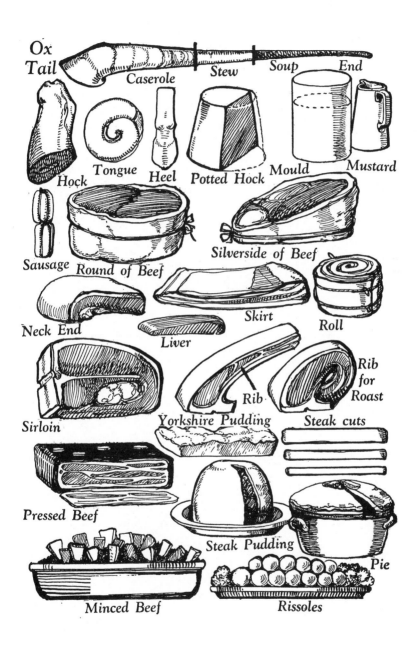

Ox Tail

Caserole Stew Soup End

Hock Tongue Heel Potted Hock Mould Mustard

Sausage Round of Beef Silverside of Beef

Neck End Liver Skirt Roll

Sirloin Rib Rib for Roast

Yorkshire Pudding Steak cuts

Pressed Beef Steak Pudding Pie

Minced Beef Rissoles

IF ONLY HE HAD
DRUNK TWO
BOTTLES ...

I STARTED drinking port when I was less than two years old. An injudicious friend remonstrated with my mother—if I had port when I was well, what could I take if I were ill and needed strengthening? She answered that it would prevent my ever being ill. I never was ill enough to spend a day in bed till I was fifty-five, and might never have been ill at all, if I had gone on drinking port proportionately; but I degenerated with the times and only drank two glasses, not two bottles, as I should. There is an entry in Dyott's Diary, 10 November 1787—'There were just twenty dined, and we drank sixty-three bottles of wine.'

from Cecil Torr (b. 1857), *Small Talk at Wreyland*, Second Series, 1921.

Two Reds
Don't Make A
White

TWO REDS DON'T
MAKE A WHITE:
I BURGUNDY

PAUL LEVY

LOVERS of red wine know that the virtues of their favourite tipple are basically either those of burgundy or those of claret. Claret freaks appreciate austerity: they look for fruit flavour disciplined by the harshness of tannin, and take their pleasures in an adult way. They know they have to wait until time has softened the tannins and mellowed them before they are rewarded. Even when drinking mature wine, they recognize that much of the pleasure takes time to achieve, and that a long-lasting finish is sometimes to be preferred to an immediate impression of fruitiness. We burgundians are more infantile.

What appeals to burgundy heads is the sweetness of the attack of the wine, the first sensations upon taking it into the mouth. We also like the complex bouquet of the mature pinot noir grape, which, though it sometimes smells of pure fruit such as raspberries or cherries, often has a decadent, corrupt, earthy smell (usually described as 'barnyard') of the sort Dr Spock tells us babies enjoy. These (to us) enjoyable smells and tastes are not confined to wines produced in Burgundy. Indeed we quite frequently find them in the clarets of St Emilion and Pomerol, with their preponderance of merlot over cabernet sauvignon grapes; and I recently found these funky, raunchy aromas and flavours in a California 1979 Firestone Cabernet Sauvignon.

I had a very rewarding week with Jean-François Bouchard, who is the ninth generation of the family firm of Bouchard, the oldest négociant in Beaune. Burgundy négociants are typically wholesale merchants of wine, buying stocks from growers and blending, maturing and bottling wine. Bouchard also owns vineyards. I particularly relished their oddly named Beaune du Château '84, a blend of pinots from odds and bobs of premier cru châteaux and a stunning '83 Nuits-St-Georges 'Clos St-Marc'.

A few days earlier I had been at a grand tasting of growers' burgundies at a London firm that boasts as one of its partners Anthony Hanson, MW, author of the best book on burgundy. We burgundians can be snobbish about our tipple, and are often to be heard saying that we prefer growers' more characterful wines to those of any but the best négociants (such as

Bouchard). The high point of the tasting was their '85s, which are, says Anthony Hanson, 'very special indeed. The grapes were ripe and healthy, the wines are rich, balanced and long. A great vintage.' The tasting bore this out, the star of the show being Lafarge's Volnay Clos du Château des Ducs, which has not been available for 40 years, and was being shown in Britain for the first time. Its fruity, clean-compost bouquet and complex taste of summer fruits make it worth its nearly £20 price—to rich burgundians, anyway.

from The Observer

TWO REDS DON'T
MAKE A WHITE:
2 CLARET

PAMELA VANDYKE PRICE

IF YOUR bank balance is favourable, you can drink a fine, even a great, claret several times a year. But, multi-millionaire though you may be, you'll still count yourself fortunate to drink a dozen truly great red burgundies in a lifetime.

The size of the two regions makes this inevitable, likewise the huge range of wines within the Bordeaux vineyard: the area characteristics, varying climates and microclimates, the complexities resulting from the 'Bordeaux mix' of several grapes, and the way in which one estate can make quite a different type of wine from its neighbour alongside. And, infinite though the subtle variations within the clarets may be, it is easier to begin to acquire some knowledge of the style of a commune and character of an estate and a vintage than it is to grapple with the nuances of domaine and growers' burgundies and those of the négoce, the difference between sliver-sized plots. (Maybe the majority of burgundy lovers don't attempt to try?)

Red burgundy certainly needs to be drunk in the context of food and, whether it's merely husky *cuisine paysanne* or *haute*, this food, often rich, unctuously sauced and substantial, asserts itself as of equal importance with the wines. The claret lover, though, is a discriminating but not gutsy feeder and, at a Bordeaux-orientated table, the fare is only a discreet accompaniment to the wines; a bottle of claret will be perfect with simple but fine roasts and grills or even down to a modest bread-and-cheese snack; you can even drink what I might term briskly fruity small-scale clarets with many fish dishes (omit the eggy sauces) without experiencing the metallic taste in the mouth that some fear in this combination. As for the 'burgundy for game', it is possible to find certain large-scale clarets from St Émilion and Pomerol that will hold their own here too and, for the finer feathered gamebirds, the essentially firm but subtly aromatic Pauillacs and red Graves are superb.

Burgundy advocates sometimes fling the adjectives 'harsh', 'bitter', 'astringent' at claret, which indicates that their choice—or that of their wine merchant—has been unfortunate. Very few claret vintages are completely 'off' these days and although the wines of even the greater years seldom require the threescore years and ten to peak, as in our grandparents' time, usually more probably achieve higher overall quality along with earlier drinkability; the masterpieces of the maker's craft among them display an adroit balance of fruit, acidity and tannin which, together with the various methods of 'handling' them for the ultimate pleasure of drinkers, makes for civilized discussion and argument—yet another pleasure claret provides.

Indeed, the occasional austerity, yielding to experienced presentation, of certain fine clarets is in itself a quiet challenge and lure—claret drinkers like to think about what they are drinking. It may be that this is a very British attitude—the reserve and then the gradual revelation as the wine opens itself are discreet, often understated qualities only perceived by the sensitive; some export markets go for a more immediate appeal in the clarets they prefer and these wines, albeit good, are not always those taken seriously and affectionately by the Anglo-Saxons.

There is, though, some truth in that the sensuality of red burgundy makes drinking it an uncomplicated pleasure. Sometimes one doesn't want a wine that makes demands, rather as one wants a 'good bad book' when convalescent. But in such circumstances I doubt that I'd opt for red burgundy or even Beaujolais. The appeal of burgundy is totally different from that of red Bordeaux and, although there are such things as 'quaffing wines' in the Gironde, if I couldn't drink them, I'd probably prefer a Shiraz from the southern hemisphere; after such a bottle it would even be possible to open a claret! As for the combining of claret and burgundy in the same meal, I have never known them go happily in tandem, even when separated by a sorbet. Both cerebrally and sensually one's mind and one's tastebuds tend to be confused. Thank heaven for the differences in the two great reds—and may we enjoy many bottles of both over which to argue as to the supremacy of each . . .

175

WHAT TO BUY
AND WHAT TO
DRINK IN 1990

CLIVE COATES M.W.

SINCE 1982 we have seen a succession of vintages which, contrary to the old laws of quality being inversely proportional to quantity, have for the most part been both abundant and successful. We have been living through a period of plenty.

Unlike in biblical times, however, these years of plenty will not be followed by vintages of famine. Mankind today can do much to mitigate the effects of a capricious nature both in the vineyard and, particularly in the winery. Vintages like 1984 and 1987 were declared 'short' by proprietors in Bordeaux but, in each, more *appellation controlée* red wine was produced than in any of the vintages of the 1960s and almost as much—within a cellar-full or two—as in 1970, at the time a record crop. Moreover, even in the so-called poor vintages, many surprisingly good wines were made—and consistently too from *petit château* to *premier cru*. I remember the poor vintages and bad wines—all I could afford at the time except on high days and holidays—when I first began to be interested in the subject in the late 1950s. Cheap wine really was cheap in those days. The most significant achievement in the world of wine in the last generation has been the virtual elimination of these sour, rank, coarse, or insipid but certainly headache-producing brews.

Today there are very few bad wines and no bad vintages. It is fair to say that no year is less than satisfactory for dry white wines and very few for reds. So for everyday drinking the latest and therefore the freshest vintage is probably the best to go for. You will rarely go wrong. And the current level of production is doing much to stabilize prices.

In the world of fine wine, life is different. Sometimes I think that those who make and deal in fine wine live in a completely artificial, almost fictional, environment. In the world of the finest wines, prices are determined not by what it costs to produce the bottles nor by what the final customer can afford, nor even, necessarily, by the quality relation between this vintage and the next—and certainly not with any consideration of the quantity of wine available. As a result, places like Bordeaux, where more red wine was produced in the five years between 1982 and 1986 than in the entire twenty vintages after the Second World War, are awash with wine. The price levels of the finest wines are higher than the market can bear.

In general, therefore, the best value can be obtained outside those regions traditionally associated with the finest wines. Search in areas such as Fronsac in Bordeaux, the Côte Chalonnaise in Burgundy, the Rhône and the best of the South of France, particularly Bandol for French red wines. Look in the Graves, the Côte Chalonnaise the lesser Côte de Beaune communes and Alsace for whites. But also cast your net outside France, to Italy, Portugal and Australia, even New Zealand.

Bordeaux

Inevitably, however, I must begin with mainstream France, and France begins with Bordeaux. Nineteen eighty-three, 1985, 1986 and 1988 have followed the superb 1982 clarets as vintages worth laying down. The 1983s were more expensive than the 1982s and the 1985s pricier still. Since then, though, there has been a modest and sensible fall. In retrospect there was little need to buy any of these *en primeur*, for whatever the opening price there has been little capital appreciation since and most of the wines are still available. Why buy before you have to? Good as these four vintages are, none is so superb as to demand cellaring. This current fetish—encouraged by wine merchants, for it provides useful advance profit and is cash-flow positive—for inundating the consumer with opening offers every single vintage needs to be resisted. Instead, if you need to, obtain earlier, more ready-to-drink vintages such as 1981, 1979 and 1978 for classed growths and the plump and luscious lesser 1982 Saint Emilions and Pomerols, or their satellites. These are relatively much better value, and the respective quality of the individual wines is more clearly established. However, *do* buy some Sauternes of the magnificent 1986 and fine 1988 vintages. Quality sweet-wine years are much less regular. Also investigate the increasing number of enterprising wine-makers in the Graves for dry whites.

It is early to judge the 1988 Sauternes but among the top 1986s I would single out Châteaux d'Arche, Broustet, Doisy-Védrines, Doisy-Daëne and Lamothe-Guignard among the *deuxièmes crus*, though Château Nairac takes the palm; and Lafaurie-Peyraguey, Rayne-Vigneau, Sigalas-Rabaud, Clos-Haut-Peyraguey and Rieussec among the *premiers*. There has been a dramatic improvement in standards among the *crus classés* in recent years in the area. Today almost all now produce wine worth considering. For Sauternes-lovers this is excellent news.

White Graves are more consistently ripe and delicious, even in 1987, a disappointing year for reds. Sadly, they take a bit of finding on the British market. Châteaux Montalivet, Roquetaillade-la-Grange, the remarkable Clos Floridene made by Denis Dubourdieu, Cruzeau and Richemorin (in the same stable as the excellent Louvière) and Larrivet-Haut-Brion are all fine but under-appreciated. Best of all is (or was until its recent change of winemaker—a question mark must temporarily hang over it) Château Rahoul, exclusive to the (Sunday Times) Wine Club. Peter Vinding-Diers, late of Rahoul, has now bought Château de Landiras, a property to watch. Most of the *crus classés*, those which formerly made undistinguished wine, have also pulled their socks up, perhaps because a re-classification was due in 1984 (it still has not surfaced). Smith-Haut-Lafitte and de Fieuzal, both classed for red but not for white, I already regard as *crus classés*. La Tour Martillac and Malartic-Lagravière are also consistently fine these days. Today, you don't have to queue up and pay horrendous prices for Laville-Haut-Brion, Domaine de Chevalier and Haut-Brion Blanc to get fine white Graves.

Burgundy

After a run of indifferent vintages since 1978—though 1979 was good for white wines and 1980 for reds—Burgundy produced a big, hefty vintage in 1983, but marred by too much dry tannin, and hail and rot in some places in the Côte de Nuits; had another disappointing vintage in 1984, and then a gift from the gods in 1985—plenty of wine, consistently high quality and charmingly, seductively, an abundance of ripe fruit. Prices hit the roof. They came down a little in 1986, where there are some excellent white wines, but rose again in 1987, not too bad a vintage but one short in quantity. The fine 1988 reds have opened with prices up by thirty per cent.

At these levels, one is tempted to tell the Burgundians to take a running jump; but where else can one find the true taste of the Pinot Noir and, indeed, Chardonnay of such elegance? And the harvest, even in abundant vintages, leaves little to go round.

The solution is to investigate the Côte Chalonnaise and, for additional whites, the lesser communes of the Côte de Beaune—the villages of Montagny, Givry, Mercurey, Rully and Bouzeron for the former and Auxey-Duresses, Saint-Aubin and Saint-Romain for the latter; and to go to a Burgundy specialist.

Bear in mind also that you may well get a much better wine under a simple 'Bourgogne' label but from a high-class domaine than something supposedly more distinguished but at an inflated price from a less reputable source. These top domaines are meticulous about separating the not-quite-so-good from the best; but the lesser *cuvées* can, nevertheless, prove excellent value for money.

The Northern Rhône and Bandol

Despite recent price increases and the worldwide fêting of those such as Gérard Jaboulet of Hermitage la Chapelle and Gérard Chave, also of Hermitage, the northern Rhône persists in producing wines of excellent value. Vintages have the happy chance of being more consistent than further north but the wines do need time. Buy your northern Rhônes for drinking in the year 2000 and beyond. Buy the excellent 1985 in preference to the good-but-not-great 1986 or 1987—if you can still obtain it. And do not miss the excitingly promising 1988s.

The wines of the southern sector of the Rhône Valley were as successful as the north in 1988, but because they are based on the Grenache grape, I find less to my personal taste than those of Bandol, a region I consider vastly underrated—and Bandol was the only area in France to produce really successful *vins de garde* in 1987, up to the high levels of 1985 and 1983. In Bandol I would single out the Bunans at Moulin des Costes and Mas de la Rouvière, the Domaine de Pibarnon, the Domaine de la Bastide Blanche and the Domaine Tempier.

Italy

Exasperating Italy! There is so much wine. Much is indifferent but, equally and increasingly, so much is good. But the wine laws are in a mess and the controls of even the best regions, those that are D.O.C.G. (*Denominazione di Origine Controllata et Garantita*)—the *garantita* part denoting approval by a tasting panel among other things—seems poorly policed, so that under a single label, Barolo for example, you can find wine that is not only abysmal but, to this outsider, surely fraudulent. Yet the best are splendid and exciting value.

There is not enough space to recommend all that is good, and worth buying, so I will confine myself to writing about one recent development outside the D.O.C. rules but of stimulating potential. In the Chianti region—the laws being what they are—many of the best wines are not officially Chianti. Some are made exclusively from Sangiovese, the Chianti grape (which is not allowed unblended.) Others from Cabernet Sauvignon. The best are from a mixture of both.

These include the well-established Sassicaia and Tignanello, and many that are not widely stocked. It is worth going to a specialist. The 1988 vintage in Tuscany is splendid.

Portugal

Strangely, I find the Portuguese reds made outside the traditional areas of Dão and Bairrada usually more individual and more interesting and hence more satisfying. Many of the best are produced from the Perequita grape (Perequita means little parrot, by the way) and by the firm of José Maria da Fonseca, no relation to Fonseca the port producers.

One of José Maria da Fonseca's wines is labelled Perequita. The Camarate is more claret-like, the Pasmados perhaps the most complex, though I also admire very much a wine called Co. Another wine worth looking for is the Reguengos de Monsarraz. I urge readers who have not tried these wines to give them a whirl—they will only set you back a fiver, if that.

Australia and New Zealand

I know that I am by no means alone in considering Antipodean wines the best value currently on the British market. The weakness of the Australian dollar may be unfortunate for antipodean lovers of claret and burgundy but it gives us a splendid opportunity to acquire a knowledge of the best that the countries can produce—at what are indeed, by French and Californian standards, amazing bargains.

It is curious that nowhere else in the world, not since the Syrah was planted in Bordeaux or claret was laced with Hermitage, has anyone had the idea of blending the wines of two of the world's three greatest black grape varieties. (The Pinot doesn't blend with anything without losing all its personality and finesse—take passetoutgrains for example).

Yet they do in Australia. The Syrah (or Shiraz) has been planted there for many years, the Cabernet Sauvignon increasingly since 1960. Each separately produces wine of personality and concentration. Together, they blend to produce a flavour and character unique to Australia.

Meanwhile, both countries and the New Zealand Sauvignons, have discovered the Chardonnay, perhaps the world's most fashionable white-wine variety. Like the Cabernet Sauvignon, the Chardonnay is a vine that seems to thrive in a range of climates and soil structures without losing its inherent individuality. I have never been that struck with Australian Rieslings though I have long admired some of their Sémillons and Australian and New Zealand Chardonnays can be obtained for upwards of little more than £5. The value puts France to shame.

What Vintages of Classic Wines to Drink in 1990
Claret.   The 1981s, best in the Médoc and the Graves, are now beginning to soften up. This is an amiable, soft-centred vintage, not too high in acidity. Quality is good but not great. Do not expect anything better than competent claret, a useful preliminary to an older, better bottle. The 1979s have turned out better than was thought at the time and this is a vintage that is consistent throughout the Bordeaux area. A good level of acidity is keeping the wines fresh and will preserve the fruit: They are now *à point* except for the biggest St-Juliens and Pauillacs. The 1978 vintage was more concentrated and more classic. After going through a phase of awkward adolescence, some of these are now coming round and showing their generosity as well as their breeding. The top wines still need keeping. Neither the 1976s nor the 1975s have fulfilled their earlier promise; the earlier vintage is too hard, the latter suffered from dilution of its concentration and acidity as a result of September rains, and many of the wines have become either attenuated or astringent. Drink your 1976s soon. Enjoy your Libournais 1975s now and hope your Médoc 1975s will still soften up. Nineteen-seventy-ones too, are beginning to show a bit of age but the best 1970s, though delicious now, will still keep

well. Those fortunate enough still to have carefully preserved 1966s, 1964s from St-Emilion and Pomerol 1962 and the magnificent 1961s, can now enjoy them in their prime. The top years prior to 1961 can still be fine and vigorous but beware of your bottles drying out. Who wants to be a necrophiliac?

Sauternes are always variable. Even in the best years some, through bad judgement of when to harvest, poor *élevage* or just luck, make disappointing bottles. The best 1975s and 1976s drink well today but can still be held. Those of 1971, 1970, the few excellent 1967s and the more consistent 1962s are, today, delicious.

Burgundy. Burgundy is so variable that it is very difficult to generalize about which recent vintages are ready and which still need keeping. Some lesser 1983 reds, even 1985 and 1986s, those from the Côte de Beaune and the Côte Chalonnaise, can already be drunk, as can all but the most sumptuous and concentrated whites of these years. The 1982 red wine vintage was abundant and only the most dedicated produced wines which were not a little loose-knit, if not now a trifle frayed at the edges—the quality/quantity inverse ratio certainly applies to the Pinot Noir. The 1979 reds are beginning to weaken, the 1980s holding up better, though neither is a great year. There are rather better bottles in the more classically balanced 1978 vintage—both red and white are now in their prime—and some fine Côte de Beaune reds in 1976—the Côte de Nuits were always a bit too dense and the whites a little heavy. Nineteen-seventy-two, 1971, 1969, 1966 and 1964 are earlier fine vintages for red wines but some bottles may now show age.

Northern Rhône. While lesser vintages obviously mature sooner, the best Syrah-based Rhône wines need at least a decade, ideally fifteen years.

This rules out classic vintages such as 1985, 1983 and 1982, even 1978 except at a pinch. Those lucky enough to possess 1976s, the fine trio of 1971, 1970 and 1969 and earlier bottles, can congratulate themselves on their foresight— for the wines, in retrospect, were absurdly cheap—and enjoy them now.

Port. Port needs twenty years, the shippers will tell us, but only recently have they begun to hold back enough true vintage (as opposed to those excellent compromises—the single *quinta* wines) so that those who are not around at the outset can acquire them later. The 1975s—a lighter vintage— are drinkable now, as are the 1970s, however and the few 1967s are also mature. The pair of 1966 and 1963 are better still, the later year never really having had the recognition it deserves while the earlier, often proclaimed a classic, now finds itself with a critic or two who will aver that it is not quite so magnificent as all that. I must demur—I find them magnificent. Both are in their prime but will last for decades. The 1955s are vigorous, rich and full of character and both 1948 and 1945 have still many years to go. Those with 1960, 1958, 1954, 1950 and 1947 should consider finishing them up.

ENVOI

STRUGNELL'S SONNET
ON THE PRICE OF SIN
WENDY COPE

The expense of spirits is a crying shame,
So is the cost of wine. What bard today
Can live like old Khayyám? It's not the same—
A loaf and Thou and Tesco's Beaujolais.
I had this bird called Sharon, fond of gin—
Could knock back six or seven. At the price
I paid a high wage for each hour of sin
And that was why I only had her twice.
Then there was Tracy, who drank rum and Coke,
So beautiful I didn't mind at first
But love grows colder. Now some other bloke
Is subsidizing Tracy and her thirst.
I need a woman, honest and sincere,
Who'll come across on half a pint of beer.

from Making Cocoa for Kingsley Amis, 1986

NOTES ON
CONTEMPORARY
CONTRIBUTORS

Kingsley Amis, CBE, b. 1922
Poet, critic and novelist (Booker Prize 1986). Contributor to *Compleat Imbiber* No. 2 (1958) and to second series (1986).

Burton Anderson, b. 1938
Brought up in Minnesota, but lived in Europe since 1962; Rome and Paris for *International Herald Tribune*, 1968–77; now resident in Tuscany; author of classic *Vino* (1980) and now working on an Italian wine atlas.

Sybille Bedford OBE FRSL, b. 1911
Educ. Italy, France and England; novelist and biographer. Recreations: wine, books and travel.

Anthony Burgess, b. 1917
Educ. Xaverian College, Manchester, sometime schoolmaster; novelist and critic. Recreations: composing and playing music (piano), cooking, languages and travel.

Lord Carrington KG, CH, KCMG, MC, b. 1919
Educ. Eton and Sandhurst. Sometime Secretary of State for Foreign Affairs, later Secretary-General NATO. Chairman Christie's.

Clive Coates, MW, b. 1941
Educ. St Paul's; Master of Wine, 1970; retired from wine trade 1984 to found specialist fine-wine magazine, *The Vine*. His book, *Claret*, published 1982.

Derek Cooper, b. 1925
Educ. Raynes Park Grammar School, Wadham College, Oxford. Author, broadcaster, journalist. Glenfiddich Wine and Food Writer of the Year 1973, 1980. Broadcaster of the Year 1984. Contributor to *Compleat Imbiber* No. 12 (1971).

Wendy Cope, b. 1945
Read history St Hilda's College, Oxford; poet and formerly school-mistress. Cholmondeley Award for Poetry 1987.

John Davies MW, b. 1931
Educ. City of London School, Corpus Christi College, Oxford. Wine Trade since early 1960s. Master of Wine 1965.

M. F. K. Fisher, b. 1908
Educ. University of California, Los Angeles, and Dijon University; many years abroad, mostly in France. Now lives in Napa Valley, the Elizabeth David of American literature.

Lady Antonia Fraser FRSL, b. 1932
Daughter of Earl and Countess of Longford; educ. St Mary's Convent, Ascot and Lady Margaret Hall, Oxford; m. Harold Pinter, playwright 1980. Novelist, biographer, historian. Sometime chairman, Soc. of Authors and Crime-Writers' Association.

John Fuller, b. 1937
Fellow of Merton College, Oxford: son of Roy Fuller, Professor of Poetry, Oxford, (and contributor to *Compleat Imbiber* second series [1986]).

Gerry Hamill, b. 1919
Educ. Our Lady of Grace Elementary School, Manchester; sometime Covent Garden Market porter.

Alan Jenkins, b. 1955
Educ. Sussex University: Fiction and Poetry editor, *Times Literary Supplement*.

Miles Kington, b. 1941
Educ. Glenalmond and Trinity College, Oxford. Sometime Literary Editor, *Punch*: later columnist *The Times*, now the *Independent*. Jazz player (double bass) Instant Sunshine group.

Paul Levy, b. 1941
Educ. Harvard and Oxford Universities: a lapsed don, now Food and Wine Editor, the *Observer* since 1980.

Humphrey Lyttelton, b. 1921
Educ. Eton and Camberwell School of Art, jazz musician and journalist. Recreations: bird-watching and calligraphy. Contributor to *Compleat Imbiber* No. 1 (1956)

James Michie
Classical scholar (Trinity College, Oxford). Publisher (Bodley Head) and poet: translated Horace, Catullus, Martial and, from the French, La Fontaine.

John Julius, 2nd Viscount Norwich, b. 1929
Son of Lord and Lady Norwich (Duff Cooper and Lady Diana Manners) educ. Eton, University of Strasbourg and New College, Oxford. Sometime

member Foreign Service; writer, film-maker, Italophile (Chairman, Venice in Peril Fund, Commendatore, Italian Order of Merit).

Frank Parrish
Pseudonymous—and prolific—novelist, who lives deep in the countryside, heavily involved in rural pursuits.

Elizabeth Ray, b. 1925
Social worker, magistrate, a director of Kent Opera, cookery correspondent, the *Observer* 1969–74, contributor to various magazines and author of four cookery books. Married Cyril Ray, 1953. Contributor to *Compleat Imbiber* Nos. 11 (1970) 12 (1971) and second series (1986).

Egon Ronay, b. Budapest
Emigrated to England 1946; originally cook and caterer; publisher restaurant and other guides since 1956 and member various British and foreign gastronomic academies.

Pamela Vandyke Price, b. 1923
Educ. Somerville College, Oxford and Central School of Speech Training and Dramatic Art. Author of twenty-five books on wine and/or food; twelve years wine correspondent of *The Times*; Chevalier du Mérite Agricole.

Vernon Scannell FRSL, b. 1922
Educ. Leeds University; soldiered with the Gordon Highlanders, Middle East and Normandy; poet and novelist (Heinemann Award 1960, Cholmondeley Poetry Prize 1974).

Ruth Silvestre
Singer and actress; restored, with husband, derelict farmhouse in Lot-et-Garonne while 'resting' in 1976. Contributor to *Compleat Imbiber*, second series (1986).

Sir Sacheverell Sitwell, Bt., CH., 1897–1989
Educ. Eton; poet and novelist since 1924 (Benson Silver Medal, Royal Society of Literature, 1981).

Auberon Waugh, b. 1939
Educ. Downside and Christ Church, Oxford; son of Evelyn Waugh (who contributed to *Compleat Imbiber* No. 6 [1963]). Editor the *Literary Review*; novelist, columnist, essayist; contributor to *Compleat Imbiber* No. 5 (1962).

B. A. Young, OBE, b. 1912
Educ. Highgate School; served World War Two in Lancashire Fusiliers, King's African Rifles and staff; *Punch* 1944–64, *Financial Times* 1964–77. Novelist, theatre critic, biographer and confectioner of light verse; contributor to *Compleat Imbiber* Nos. 3 (1960), 5 (1962), 7 (1964), 8 (1965) and 9 (1967).

ACKNOWLEDGEMENTS

The Wine-Snob's . . . by kind permission of A. P. Watt Ltd. on behalf of The Council of Trinity College, Oxford

. . . The Wine-Lover's C. Sybille Bedford 1968 Published by Virago Press 1984

. . . The Wine Merchant's by kind permission of Egon Ronay

. . . The Enthusiastic Amateur's by kind permission of the editor of *Punch*

. . . The Non-Starter by kind permission of Anthony Shiel Associates Ltd.

The Gourmet's Love Song by kind permission of A. P. Watt Ltd. on behalf of the estate of the late P. G. Wodehouse

'A pity that one cannot buy it in England' by kind permission of David Higham Associates Ltd.

'Yorghti!' by kind permission of The Society of Authors as the literary representative of the estate of Compton Mackenzie.

Variation on a Horatian Theme (the James Michie translation) by kind permission of David Higham Associates Ltd.

Hemingway and Wine by kind permission of the editor-in-chief of Italian Wines and Spirits (*Civilta del Bere*)

Duff's Drinking Life and My Father's Cellar by kind permission of Simon Berry, and Berry Bros and Rudd Ltd

Nostalgia by kind permission of William Heinemann Ltd.

Poet's Picnic by kind permission of John Fuller

Down Under, From Up Here by kind permission of the *Observer* News Service

A Ploughman's at the Pub by kind permission of Derek Cooper

It isn't all Baloney in Bologna by kind permission of the editor of *Punch*

Nobody Knows the Truffles I've Seen by kind permission of the editor of the *Sunday Times* Wine Club magazine

Mediterranean Feast by kind permission of the editor of the *Sunday Times*

A Nice Cup of Tea by kind permission of A. M. Heath Ltd

Cupid's Nightcap by kind permission of the *Statesman* and Nation Co., Ltd.

Monsieur Dodin-Bouffant Makes an End of It by kind permission of Faber and Faber Ltd.

The Bresse Chicken, translation © by Anne Drayton by kind permission of Penguin Books

THE ILLUSTRATIONS

Most illustrations in this anthology are from the collections of Christopher Fielden, Holt, Trowbridge, Wiltshire; Peter Cooper, London NW3; and the publishers.

For kind permission to reproduce other illustrations the publishers are indebted to the following:

p.39 Vanessa Binns: taken from Feasting by Brian Binns
p.42 Sogrape
p.57 The Hon. Simon Howard: taken from a print from the Castle Howard Collection
pp.67, 91, 144 and 162 Ebury Press, a division of Century Hutchinson: taken from Good Housekeeping Country Cooking by Elizabeth Ray
p.73 Australian Tourist Commission: taken from The Official Koala Handbook
p.77 Regimental Adjutant, Grenadier Guards
p.78 Ward Lock Ltd, Cassell PLC: taken from the British Country Cheeses by Pamela Westland
p.82 Italian Tourist Office
p.88 Syndicat des Producteurs de Truffes, Pêrigord
p. 123 Hereford Cider Museum Trust